Our Homestead Story

By Mr. and Mrs. Stephen B. Castleberry

Castleberry Farms Press

Second Edition
© Copyright 2003
Castleberry Farms Press
P.O. Box 337
Poplar, WI 54864

ISBN 1-891907-12-3

Printed in the U.S.A.

To Robin Berglund, whose friend-ship, incredible helpfulness, and patience over the years has been most appreciated.

Steve and Susie Castleberry

Our Homestead Story

Table of Contents

A Note From the Authors

Writing a book about your life is fun and also a little scary. It is fun to know that you are writing down a history that will probably end up being a treasure for your great-great- grandchildren. It is also fun to be able to record the many acts of kindness and love that we have been the recipients of over the last few years. So what makes it scary? That we have left someone out and will remember it about two weeks after the book is printed. Or that we have written something to which someone might take offense. If we are guilty on either count, please forgive us.

Some people might think we moved here just to get some material to write this book. Hardly! We can think of lots easier topics on which to write a book than living a more self-sufficient lifestyle. Actually, we never even thought of writing this book until one of our friends suggested we jot down our experiences.

You'll notice that the book is written in first person, with Steve as the speaker. That doesn't mean that Susie didn't help write the book. We are a team, and work together on most everything. That's the way it's supposed to be. We wrote it in first person primarily to make the book more enjoyable to read.

As you read this book, you may say to yourself, "I could never do that! It would be too hard." Or, "I'm not an expert. I'm sure it wouldn't work for me." Maybe you couldn't do some things we have written about. But you can probably do a lot more than you think. And forget that only experts can do certain things. That's a fairly new idea in our culture. In the good old days people did pretty much everything themselves. Don't be afraid to tread where only "experts" walk.

On the other hand, you may read parts of this book and say to yourself, "I know a much better way to do it than that! What makes the Castleberrys think they're experts?" We're not experts and we freely admit it. We're learning, every single day, and hope to continue learning for many years to come. One thing we have learned is that much of what we have tried is more art than science. There usually is not one best way to do things. If you see an error in what we've done, chances are that we are discovering the error ourselves right about now. I suppose we could just wait until we have all the correct answers. Naw, we'd never write the book if we did that!

Now for the disclaimer: This book is intended to provide an account of our first few years of homesteading and what has worked/not worked for us. However, it's not intended to be a medical manual, replace the electrical code, etc. Thus, before you try copying any of our activities please make sure you know what you are doing. Plans may have to be altered to meet local codes or zoning ordinances. We caution you not to attempt any potentially dangerous activities without competent professional assistance. You get the idea. Also, we haven't, in most instances, given you a blow-by-blow description of how to accomplish something. There are excellent how-to books that do that (See our Recommended Readings List in the back for a list of some). We have just attempted to share with you the beginning of our pilgrimage toward more self-sufficiency with God's help.

We hope you enjoy reading Our Homestead Story. There's an order form on the last page for this and other books we've published.

Our son Ben was just eighteen months old when this story begins. The picture on the front cover is our Ben, driving the tractor last summer at the age of 11. Enjoy your children! They grow up fast.

Steve and Susie Castleberry
May 2003

Chapter One
Cows Will Be Cows

What do you mean, 'Uncle Jim is at the door'?" I asked, struggling to turn over and look at the clock by the bed. It's 6:30 on a Saturday morning. The youngest children are still sleeping quietly. I got to bed a little later than I had hoped last night. And now Jeannie is anxiously telling me that my friend is at the door and needs to see me *right now*! As I start to crawl out of bed she continues, "Daddy, Uncle Jim said the cows are out on the state highway." Suddenly I'm fully awake, pulling on pants, trying to get on socks at the same time I am putting on a shirt. It doesn't work well.

Reaching the front door, I find Jim already turning around in my driveway preparing to head back toward the road. As he drives by, he leans out the window: "The cows are **way** down the road." How can he sound so calm? He heads out to try and keep them from running further.

I tell Jeannie (11) and Stevie (9), my two oldest children, to get the calf halters from the barn, and we quickly hop into my van. We drive about a mile down the road, passing a dead porcupine as we go. "Hey! Did you see that neat porcupine on the road? Can we look at it later?" Children don't have any trouble setting priorities. It's just that their priorities often don't coincide with ours. "We're looking for calves right now, so just keep your eyes open," I reply.

Down a slope, back up the other side, and then, there they were.

You couldn't miss them! Lights flashing on Jim's car, the car parked smack-dab in the middle of the road, and Jim hobbling around on a pair of crutches trying to corral the runaways - they weren't hard to spot! I parked my van on the side of the road and the four of us started numerous attempts to capture our prey. Ever try to catch a frisky calf that has been waiting for this chance to frolic on a busy state highway? It's not easy! We finally managed to halter Brownie and Spot (a couple of Jersey calves) but Todd would not be caught so easily.

Todd requires a bit of explanation. Our good neighbors, Martin and Bev Bitner, along with their son Todd and his wife Becky, live just across the hayfield from us. They have a large dairy farm of Holstein cows, and they (the Bitners, not the cows) befriended us shortly after we moved in. Martin's hard work, Bev's motherly kindness, Becky's cheerful smile, and Todd's crazy sense of humor made them special to us. That first autumn, Martin had knee surgery and Todd needed help milking, so the older children and I went over to help out with chores for a while. A few weeks later, on a cold snowy day near Christmas, a beautiful little black and white calf arrived in our barn with a big red bow around his neck. The calf was the Bitners' way to thank us for our help. The children immediately named the little calf "Todd" in honor of their hero, Todd Bitner.

The name, however, made for some confusing and fun dinner-table conversation (like this example between my children and Susie, my wife):

Stevie: "Todd seems to have an awfully bad cough. Wonder if he could be sick?"
Susie: "You know, there is a lot of flu going around."
Stevie: "Flu? How could he get the flu?"
Jeannie: "Maybe he just swallowed milk down the wrong way."
Susie: "Was he drinking milk when you saw him?"
Stevie: "Of course he was. He's always drinking milk, Mommy. And boy, was he slobbering it everywhere today!"
Susie (after a minute of thought): "Oh, you mean Todd the *calf*!"

Finally, we devised a system for keeping matters straight. We began calling them Todd-the-Calf and Todd-the-Human. Todd-the-Human cooperated beautifully, with his usual irrepressible humor. The phone would ring and a voice would say, "This is Todd-the-Human. Can I speak to Steve?" Or sometimes, "This is Todd-the-Calf. When are you going to install a private line in the barn?"

Todd-the-Calf came to us at only three weeks old, and was bottle-fed for months by the children. Being the only animal we had, he didn't realize for quite some time that he was actually a cow, and not one of us. Todd had never seen a cow (that he could remember) when we got Brownie and Spot a few months later, and was so afraid of them that he ran right through the fence. Our solution was to introduce them to each other slowly, putting Spot and Brownie in one pen in the barn with Todd in an adjoining pen. Good plan. They became good friends. Partners, you might say. Todd was a large Holstein calf, and Holsteins are a bit more, oh, shall we say, high-strung? He developed quite a reputation for living on the "wild side." He became the ringleader of the bunch.

Anyway, since he wouldn't let us get close enough to halter him there on the highway, we had to grab a 25 foot-long nylon tow rope from the van and lasso the silly buckaroo. How are *your* lassoing skills? Not having been raised on a ranch out in Montana, mine were slim to none. Finally, we had all three in their calf halters. Jeannie, Stevie, and I started walking them the mile down the highway to our farm. Of course that dead porcupine *was* kind of hard to pass up, but we managed to keep our noses to the grindstone.

As we started down a hill, the calves decided this would be a good time to crank up the speed. "Don't let them run!" I shouted to the children. Seriously now, what kind of advice is that for children who weigh about a fifth of what their calf weighs? However, the calves soon tired of running. After all, they had been running all over the countryside for the last couple of hours. As we crested the top of the hill, I wondered what else could possibly happen.

Rain. Slowly at first, then more and more. Looking behind me I saw Uncle Jim following us in his car, lights flashing, and now with his windshield wiper blades going. He waved. I waved back.

Finally, we (the calves, me, the children, and Jim's car) started down our long driveway. First one and then another of the cows seemed to sort of sense that we were home again. So they . . . well, they sort of saluted; saluted in that special way that cows do. Right in the middle of the driveway. Thanks boys.

Walking the 1/4 mile of fence line in the calves' pasture (we were wet now, what difference did it make to get wetter?) we found the place they had used for the "Great Escape," and put up a strong welded cow panel as well as three strands of barbed wire to keep them in. You can't imagine the determination and conquering grins on our faces. "They sure won't get out this way again!" And it worked. At least they didn't get out *that* way for their next escape. No, the next time they just walked right out the front barn door.

Why is it that cows (and all other animals) can know immediately when a barn door is left open, but the children who left it open can never, ever seem to remember leaving it open?

This time it was a Sunday morning. Brownie and Spot headed across the state highway and saluted in Jeff's driveway. Jeff is *not* a farmer. Thanks again, boys. Todd, the ringleader calf, somehow got stuck inside our hayfield fence and couldn't figure out how to join his outlaw friends on the highway. Instead, he simply mooed his suggestions to them over the fence.

We were all awake, already dressed for church and didn't know anything was up. "Hey, what's going on?" said one of the children, suddenly noticing a commotion on the highway. It kind of looked like a busy mall parking lot filling up the morning after Thanksgiving, with cars streaming in and parking one after another. Since we don't have any shopping malls within half an hour of our house, I cleverly figured out that something was up. When I went outside, I heard someone say *something* about cows.

Well, we were in the thick of it in no time. "Get the calf

halters!" I yelled to the children while the rest of us ran for the calves. A few of the people jumped out of their cars to help, while others just sat in their cars and enjoyed the show. The "show" was perhaps enlivened by the fact that Susie, even though she had on her high heel church shoes and was seven months pregnant, was chasing the calves too.

Finally, the calves were back in the barn. How thankful I was that God had protected us from harm, and kept the calves from being hit by a car. After all, some of the cars driving around today are worth more than my whole farm! And that includes the value of our bull calves, Todd, Spot and Brownie. But perhaps I am getting ahead of myself. Let me back up a bit and tell you a little about how we got where we are.

Chapter Two
How We Got Our Farm

I wasn't raised on a farm or anywhere near one. I grew up in a suburb of Chattanooga, Tennessee and only "raised" three kinds of animals. We bought goldfish twice, but they only lived one day each time. Later, I worked at a retailer that sold tiny turtles. We were instructed by the government to kill all our turtles because of some weird disease. Instead, I brought them home and "played" with the 30 turtles until I tired of them in about two or three days. What can you *do* with turtles? Of course my family also had two dogs as I grew up, mongrels named Twister and Charlie Brown.

Susie, my wife, also grew up in suburbia. Geographically, her early years were more varied than mine with stops in Illinois, Missouri, Texas, and Tennessee. However, she only had a few dogs for family pets. And she had no farm experience at all, unless you count staying with a baby sitter that lived on a farm.

So where did this idea come from to live on a farm and try to be self-sufficient? Believe it or not, it all started outside Chicago. I was an endowed professor at a university there with a prestigious job, wonderful benefits, and a challenging, rewarding career. We were living in a rented farm house about two miles from campus that included an old barn and several old outbuildings. I don't know how to explain it, but we both started finding the "farm" life kind of neat. We spent lots of time trying to conjure up images of what it must have looked like 50 years earlier, when it was a diversified and flourishing farmstead. Now, "the farm" just consisted of a rental house, a barn in need of repair, a nice metal machine shed, and a few other old outbuildings. The 30 acres or so of cropland was planted in sweet corn each summer. In fact, you may have eaten some of that corn because it was all processed into Del Monte cream- style canned corn. The owner, Bob Twombly, told us many stories of what life was like growing up on his farm. It was quite diversified with the usual array of chickens, pigs, horses, field crops, etc. As he talked, our interest in farming only increased.

Then we started watching the farmers plowing, discing, and planting their fields. It was so neat! Things actually grew right out of the ground. Harvesting time was also incredibly interesting. We asked questions and learned about how things worked; at least we learned how the "big" farms and the big farm machinery worked. We also attended an old-fashioned tractor show and fell in love with the old way of doing things.

I guess the thing that really opened our eyes was the *Small Farmers Journal* (SFJ). Susie bought me a subscription to SFJ for Christmas one year. I tried to act happy and excited (don't you hate having to do that?) but wasn't sure I was going to like it. The subtitle of SFJ is "featuring Practical Horse-Farming," and I didn't see myself as some horse farmer. Sounded like hard, dirty work to me. Besides, everything I had ever read said, "You have to get big in farming, or you might as well get out." I started reading the first issue and found I couldn't put it down. It wasn't only about horse farming, but included articles about living a more self-sufficient life style.

The philosophy is perhaps best summarized in SFJ's slogan: ***Get Small, Go Slow, Mix It Up, And Care***. The slogan speaks to several aspects of a self-sufficient lifestyle. It pays to be small, not large, contrary to what the U.S. Department of Agriculture generally recommends. It also bucks the trend of mega-farming. Several examples I read about recently include milking 2100 cows around the clock on a farm in California, running a 1.5 million layer hen farm in Iowa, or a Texas feedlot farm with over 30,000 cattle. SFJ's slogan also states that you're better off going slow, not jumping into things too quickly and perhaps going in debt in the process. Diversity, or "mixing it up," is preferred to just having one crop or animal on your farm. Finally, you need to take care of your land, your animals, and your equipment. You also need to care about others around you and make sure they have what they need. A neat philosophy, or so it seems to us.

I was hooked. I ordered all 36 or so back issues of the

journal still in print. I started checking out books from the library and talking to people about the old ways of farming. I was really hooked.

We planted a small garden at our rental farm and I got to plow (okay, it was just a WalMart rototiller, but it was still plowing to me!), plant, weed, and harvest. The food had flavor. So did the sweet corn we picked out of Bob's fields and the apples we picked off his trees. I was really, really hooked.

My landlord realized my growing love of the farm and even decided to let me start seeing what real farm life was like. Our rental farmstead had a number of large woodchucks scurrying around. If you have never seen one, the best way to describe them is to say that they are cute, short, furry animals that everyone falls in love with. Except farmers. Seems the little critters like to dig tunnels right next to barn foundations, causing the barns to come tumbling down. Well, my landlord didn't want his barn to topple over in the next windstorm. So he suggested that I get a little practice shooting my .22 caliber rifle at them. After all, that's part of what being a farmer is about.

I eagerly accepted his assignment, and one morning Stevie and Jeannie spotted a plump prospect for me. I shot at it, and watched the little critter scurry back to the barn. "Shhhhhhhhhhh" someone was saying. No, it wasn't someone. It was something. It was a tire leaking air out of a .22 caliber hole on one of Bob's discs (that's a thing you hook to the back of the tractor to break up the soil). Sure enough the tire went totally flat. So did my ego.

When Bob came out he had a good laugh (a *really* good laugh, I should say), we got the tire off and I got it repaired. Later that summer he asked me if I had shot any more groundhogs (another name for those cute woodchucks). "Nope, I can't afford it. It cost me $20 to get that tire fixed," I said. "Well," Bob laughed, "I sure got $20 of fun out of it. It was worth it." He agreed to pay for any tires I might damage, but I didn't get any more clean shots off.

Now the search for a farm of our own began in earnest. We worked with a real estate agent, drove all over the countryside, and even put notes in some mail boxes which said "If you ever decide to sell your farm, please call Steve Castleberry at . . ." At that time, DeKalb county had a rule at that time that no new houses could be built on less than 40 acres (except for houses in subdivisions, of course). The land alone would have cost us about $200,000! We could have bought the beautiful, well-maintained farmhouse we were living in, with all five acres of grass and outbuildings around it for a mere $250,000. Somehow, it just didn't seem wise, especially since we wanted to be totally out of debt. Also, we weren't thrilled with a few other things about the area: the violent crime and gangs moving into our community from Chicago, the chemicals that were sprayed all the time on the corn and soybeans, the nuclear power plant located nearby, radon in the public water supply (although we had a well at the farmhouse), the constant threat of tornados, etc.

Even though it looked bleak, I'm not one to give up easily. In fact, I actually like a challenge. When I was in college, I went to the North Carolina mountains for a week of snow skiing instruction. The first morning out, the instructor had us all line up in one long line and said, "We're going to teach you how to ski. We'll divide you into two groups, a "fast" group and a "regular speed" group. Some of you will probably want to push yourselves hard and learn quickly. If that describes you, just push yourself forward and I'll start teaching you the basics on an accelerated schedule." You guessed it. I pushed myself forward, as did about ten other students. Some of us fell down as we pushed forward, so it's not like we already knew how to ski. It's just that we were the kind of people who like to set a challenging goal for ourselves and then work hard to achieve it. Well, in the same way I was committed to finding a farm for my family.

Since I couldn't find any farms locally, I more or less took matters into my own hands. I jumped on the job market to see what was out there. The professor market was sort of "tight" due to shrinking state budgets and the economy, but I was invited to the University of Minnesota at Duluth for an interview and accepted. The night before we were to leave for the campus visit, Steve Rubenfeld, the department head from UMD, called and said it was snowing a little but didn't look like anything to worry about. Duluth was only an eight-hour drive away and we weren't concerned about whether or not we could make it.

The next morning we left the house at around 6:00 a.m. all excited, as you can imagine. As we drove further north, we heard on the radio about some bad snow storm and that Superior was closed. "What is 'Superior'?" I thought. I looked at the map and it turned out to be the city right next to Duluth. How can a town be closed? It's easy. All you have to do is dump more than three feet of snow in a short period of time and everything comes to a standstill. Even with snowplows, snow graders, salt and everything else! I stopped at a rest area in central Wisconsin and called UMD. Steve, the department head, answered the phone, even though the university was officially closed. He was glad to hear from us, since he had been trying to call us before we left home. When he learned that we were already on the road, he suggested for our personal safety, we not try to drive to Duluth in this weather. But it would have been hard to turn around and head back home, because the storm was getting stronger and was now also behind us. We had already driven too far.

So we stopped at a motel in Bloomer, Wisconsin for the night. By this time, the wind was howling and the snow was coming down hard. It sure felt good to be snug in that warm motel room with the blizzard howling outside. Next morning the motel manager said he was sorry but that we would have to check out, because the motel was already booked for a wedding. With nowhere else to go we headed to Duluth. It was unbelievable. Snow was so deep that the roads were officially closed. Four-wheel drive vehicles were off in the ditches and tractor trailers were jackknifed off the side of the road. We prayed, let most of the air out of the tires of our full size van (for some reason I felt like I could get better traction that way - I have since learned that's not a good idea), and drove *slowly*. Our van did not have four-wheel drive. Our five children, aged 10 and under, were amazingly quiet all day. That evening they told us that they had been praying most of the time. It took us eight hours to travel only 120 miles but we finally made it.

You can't imagine how we felt when we parked our car next to the Holiday Inn. We had made it through the snow storm and terrible road conditions by God's protective and gracious care. Now we were at the hotel, with warm food, comfortable beds, a large heated swimming pool, and just about everything else you could ask for. The biggest relief was that we were no longer on a deserted portion of highway with a blizzard howling just outside the windshield.

When the university finally reopened after the snowstorm, the interview went well. Several months later I was offered the job, and I accepted. One reason I accepted was because we had looked at a few farms during my interview visit and were overwhelmed by the relatively low prices and pretty barns. Of course anything looks pretty covered in over three feet of snow (that amount is not an exaggeration). We stayed in constant contact with our real estate agents (one in Minnesota and one in Wisconsin). We finally decided on one specific week to drive up and choose a farmstead. That's risky. Basically, you only have the opportunity to buy what is on the market at that time. But we had little choice, since there were no acceptable rental houses and no rental farms (and we didn't want to rent an apartment--it's kind of hard to start farming in one). Both agents sent us all kinds of information about farms and farmland for sale. Finally, the week arrived.

Gregg Hoffman, our Minnesota real estate agent, showed us a 40-acre farm, with a beautiful barn, a double car garage with remote control doors, a house that was in nearly perfect condition, all at a price that was very attractive. We didn't have a chance to look it over really carefully because it was very foggy and windy, and another agent was bringing a couple to look at it in a few minutes. What would you do in that situation? We signed a contract for it and put down earnest money that night! Boy, were we relieved to have our farm. Now we could start all of the planning for our move and life on our new farm.

In the hotel room late that night after the children were asleep, we suddenly started asking ourselves all kinds of questions. "What are the neighbors like? Is it always windy on top of that hill? What are the fields like? Is the soil rocky? Can you hear the sound of the nearby freeway all the time? Are there other farms and farmers in the area?" Those were the questions we thought of in just the first few minutes, but you get the picture. Not much sleep that night.

My sleep was also hampered because I kept thinking about an apartment I rented in Rome, Georgia, years ago. It was a beautiful brick quadplex, priced very reasonably. I couldn't really understand why the rent was so low when it was in such good condition. I fell into bed late the night I moved in, exhausted as only a move can make you. At around 2:00 a.m. I suddenly woke up to a strange light moving back and forth across the bedroom. It was getting brighter and bigger every second. It kept moving, back and forth. Was I having a nightmare because I was so tired? My racing heart sure seemed real to me. Then I nearly jumped out of my skin as a loud piercing scream sounded right outside my window! It screamed again and again. What was going on? Before I completely passed out, I perceived the sound of train wheels on a track and realized that there must be a train track right outside my window. The next morning I checked it out, and sure enough, the track was only about 75 feet from my front window. I hadn't noticed it because it was across the road and behind a few trees. Every night at 2:00 a.m. the train's lights shined in my window, and the warning whistle was given right across from my apartment. I had a better understanding of why my rent was lower than I had expected. I forgot, however, to tell Susie about the train when we got married. The first night home from our honeymoon she got a real thrill too. Sorry, dear! After that experience I knew the importance of looking things over very carefully before committing to them! Which is what I should have remembered to do before signing a contract on the farm in Minnesota.

In the morning, I got up early (you might even say I never really slept that night), left the hotel, and drove out to the farm we had bought. The fog had cleared and I found we had a "beautiful" view of Interstate 35 (along with the "beautiful" sound of traffic). The area looked very rocky. Could we grow things in that soil? The neighbors were not farmers. In fact, it looked like we were the only farm in sight. Then again there was that golf course on the other side of our property. Is that the atmosphere we were looking for in which to raise cows and maybe even pigs? Driving around the area, I found an abandoned house at the dead end of the next road over (but just through the woods back behind our barn) with the words "PARTY HOUSE" smeared in bold black letters on the side.

Party house? Suddenly, I wasn't feeling so good. Why hadn't we taken the time to check out soil conditions? Why had we rushed so much? I think it's because we so very much wanted to buy a farm and get started with our life. I called my agent. He had not had the chance to present our offer to the sellers. "What? Do you mean you haven't given them our earnest money and contract yet?" I asked. "No, I'm sorry, but you just signed it late last night at the hotel," he said, kind of apologizing. "Well, don't give it to them! We've decided not to take it," I said. I then explained our reasons and thoughts. Gregg is a true professional and one of the sharpest men I have ever met. He said it would be no problem and tore up my check so I could hear ripping over the phone. That was one of the sweetest sounds I have ever heard!

But now it was almost time to head back home. We had no farm. We didn't really have any time to drive back up from Chicago again and look for one. Our elation was turning to depression for me. Before returning home, we decided to look closely at one Wisconsin farm again. "Susie, the house would need a lot of work, it only has three small bedrooms, and a tiny kitchen, . . . yet I do love the big barn," I summarized. As we talked about it, the more we realized that it could be fixed up and renovated for our use. Also, it was nice to know that it was a "real" farm (a beef farm, but totally set up for milking cows also) located around other "real" farms. So we looked at the farm again. We even called in a contractor to give us a rough estimate of what it would cost to do the major renovations we thought it needed. The contractor was only too happy to oblige. I'll never forget him sitting on the couch punching buttons on his calculator as Susie and I watched with bated breath. Finally, he pushed back his paper and looked up with his answer. The rough bid for just the major overhaul of the house was more than $100,000 (the asking price for the whole farm and house was only $69,000)! Thanks, but no thanks.

Driving home, we turned things over again and again. Susie thought of some new ideas for renovating that wouldn't be so costly. After returning home, we talked to our Wisconsin agent, Linda Byrka, and she suggested we make an offer on the farm. We went through the usual offer- counter-offers, via the fax machine until we came to an agreement with the sellers. We signed all of the papers through the mail and it became our farm.

A few questions remained, however. Like, how much is this revised remodeling actually going to cost us? How far is this farm exactly from my job at the university? What are the neighbors like? Okay, so we still weren't perfect farm shoppers but at least we had asked lots more questions. Also, you some-times have to act based on the limited information you have because you don't have time to gather other information. My advice is to take your time, ask every question you can think of, pray about it, think about it a lot, and then make an offer.

Keep in mind that we didn't have a clue as to what we would be doing on the farm (in the income-producing sense of the word). Would we be raising beef cows, sheep, chickens, pigs, or market vegetables? Or would we take the plunge and milk cows? Would we become bee keepers or sell organic apples? What about exotic things like raising ostriches, keeping elk and selling their horns each year, or milking sheep?

We had no idea. We did know we wanted to be diversified (we can thank *Small Farmer's Journal* for that perspective). That means do a little of everything. Sort of like the old days of farming. Then, if times get bad in one thing you have other things to fall back on. We did know that we wanted to be as self-sufficient as possible, raising our own food, and our newly-purchased farm offered that possibility.

As time went on, we developed a list of "reasons" for living on a farm. These still help us as we make decisions about our lifestyle and activities. Here they are, in no particular order.

Our farm is a place where:
1. Our children can work alongside their parents.
2. We can raise healthy, wholesome food.
3. We can become less dependent on companies that support causes we don't believe in, and large corporations in general.
4. We can have more of a sense of self-sufficiency.
5. We can get good exercise and have less stress.
6. We can breathe purer air and have a healthier environment.
7. We can enjoy animals.

We also wondered how we would "fit in" in the country. Would people accept us? Would we be comfortable? Or would we be totally out of our element, like I once felt, driving down 5th Avenue and Wall Street in New York City, looking for a parking space? There are no parking spaces there! Only time would tell.

We drove back up to the farm about three months before we planned to move in, so we could "close" the house. We decided to make a week of it (it was during Spring Break at my university) and start the renovation process while there. We were scheduled to close a few days after our arrival and planned on staying in a hotel nearby. "You don't need to do that! Just stay in the farmhouse," said Ron and June Askegaard, the farm owners. "We'll be pretty much moved out by then anyway." So we did.

Have you ever camped in an empty house before? Sleeping bags on the floor, no tables, one chair, no curtains on the windows? If you have, you know that children love it! And parents endure it. We had running water (red, rusty water - we would take care of that later with a water softener), but no stove or refrigerator. We did have heat and were warm and cozy in our sleeping bags.

Our early efforts at renovating that week involved painting ceilings and walls. We will never forget Ben (then 16 months old) busily taking the paint stirrer and eating the paint off it. It probably tasted like the rusty water, so how could he know better? Why, before the closing took place, we had the place looking, . . . well, actually about the same.

Ahh, closing. Doesn't that bring warm and fuzzy thoughts to your mind? Attorneys, money, signing papers, real estate experts, more money, banks, surveys, signing more papers, more money, title searches, escrows, prorating taxes, more attorneys, signing more papers, more money, etc. We had closed on two other houses in our lives and were expecting more of the same kinds of hassles. But it was not to be. The closing took place on our kitchen counter (remember, there was no table in the house and only one chair), no attorneys were present, the owners didn't show up because they had already signed all their paperwork, and we were done in about five minutes. Mostly it was a time to chat with Gloria Olson, the realtor representing the Askegaard's, and learn more about the best places to buy fuel oil, how garbage service worked, etc. I was beginning to love the country life!

After closing we dug into renovating in earnest. We bought more paint (Ben had to have something to eat, didn't he?) and painted things that we would later just have to repaint. Ever try to paint without a ladder? It is not highly recommended.

Painting the living room ceiling was high on our priority that week for three reasons: ① It had little silver glitter things embedded in it which wasn't exactly to our tastes, ② It was dirty, and ③ It's all we had to stare at as we lay in our sleeping bags, and I wanted to stare at something clean and white! Those ceilings looked great when we were done. I'll have to admit that the place was "looking up" a little bit.

During that week we had decided to add two small additions to our farmhouse, as well as put on a new roof (it currently had three different roofing materials on it, in various shades and colors). We called two different contractors to give us an estimate. That is what the books say you are supposed to do, and we were going to do things by the book! The first estimate was almost twice what the second estimate was for. I looked at the materials specified in both proposals and found them to be exactly the same. I talked to one of the real estate agents about the contractors. In the end, we went with the cheaper bid.

The contractor estimated that he would be completely done with the renovation before we arrived in a few months to move in. That sounded great to us. So we went home, finished up our responsibilities at our old place, packed, threw out stuff, and had a huge yard sale. The day or so before we left, though, I got a rather unwelcome phone call from the contractor. "We were digging for your new basement and I'm afraid we hit the septic tank. We also hit the water line to the barn and the one to the house. Oh, and we hit the cistern, too. The county says that we can't put in a new septic tank because you have pure clay, so we'll have to put in a holding tank. It'll cost around $4000." "Well, that's just peachy," I thought. "What options do we have?" I asked. "None, really," he said. "Okay, go ahead," I answered.

Two things were frustrating to me. First, I had a diagram of where all of those things were supposed to be and none should have been hit. But I guess our diagram wasn't real accurate. Second, if the contractor was only just now digging the basement out, the chances of his being through with all renovations before we arrived in a few days were, . . . well, zero! I'm not a licensed contractor, but even I can figure that one out.

On moving day, with the help of several good friends, we filled up two Ryder trucks plus our van (and still had to leave two mattresses and some furniture behind), and headed to our new place. It took us two days to travel there. As we neared our destination, a large sign loomed ahead. As I got closer, I read the sign and got a little concerned. It read, "Weigh Station, 3/4 Mile, Left Lane." Now, here's a quick pop quiz. If you are driving a huge Ryder truck, do you have to stop at weigh stations? Quick, quick, tell me your answer! The next sign said "All trucks must enter the weigh station." Does that mean us too? Since we didn't know, we pulled in. The guys inside gave us a dirty look and motioned us emphatically to move on out. Even my mom, driving our full-sized van, pulled on the scales--we didn't want to get separated. The guys inside were not impressed. Oh well, just trying to obey the laws.

Finally, down the state highway, over several rivers, and

there was our big red barn! Elation at being "home" quickly turned to disappointment for me as we pulled into our driveway and had nowhere to park our vehicles. Construction vehicles and stuff were everywhere in the yard and driveway. The house was not ready. The basement wasn't even totally dug. Red mud was everywhere! What happened to the beauty? It must have been the snow that was so beautiful!

Some guys were still trying to break up the huge concrete cistern with sledge hammers. Taking in the view, I instantly realized that we were a long way from being "set up," realized that we were going to have cost overruns, realized that the house was not ready and thus we had nowhere to put our stuff, and realized that my family was very hungry.

The most amazing thing is that my children were overjoyed! They didn't see all the negatives that I did. Instead, they focused on the positive things--we had our farm, we could get animals soon, we would have room to play, there was a neat red barn, there were trees (a precious commodity where we moved from), construction workers and big machinery were everywhere to watch, and they were through being cooped up in a car for two days! Aren't you glad there are enthusiastic, happy children in the world? I am.

We drove to town (about 20 minutes away) to eat at Kentucky Fried Chicken. At least the children ate. I don't remember eating anything. As we left the restaurant, a man was standing there looking at our license plate. "I notice that you are from Illinois. Are you vacationing?" he asked. "No, we just moved here," was my weak, and somewhat sad reply. "Well, welcome to Wisconsin!" he exclaimed enthusiastically. "I sure hope you will enjoy living here!" Suddenly I felt better. I felt welcome and like I was really home, living in a nice place with good people. My attitude changed almost 180 degrees. Maybe God put that man there as a special blessing to our family. Thank you, sir, whoever you are!

We returned to the farm and moved a lot of construction materials so we could back the truck up to unload. I called some of my "new" fellow professors at UMD. They came out and we starting unloading most of the stuff that had to go in the house. Things were looking up. Of course, we had to store lots of boxes in the garage because the house wasn't finished. At least I had a dry, clean garage to use, for which I was thankful.

Then, it happened. Neighbors started arriving, getting out of their trucks, pulling on gloves. "What can we move? What needs to be done? How can we help?" The Berglunds invited us to supper that evening, which we quickly accepted! After a delicious meal, they took us on a much-needed, relaxing, beautiful little walk through their woods and by the Middle River that adjoins their land.

The Berthiaumes kept asking us questions about how things were going and what our needs were. Later that first evening, Sandee Berthiaume showed up at our front door with the following: a jug of hot water for us to bathe with (our hot water heater wasn't working), popcorn and a popper (for a little snack that evening), eggs, venison sausage and juice (for breakfast the next morning), an electric skillet to cook breakfast on (we didn't have a stove), and an invitation for us to use their shower anytime we needed it ("Really, it won't be a problem at all. We hardly ever use that bathroom anyway. You can use it anytime you want to.") Others stopped by and offered us assistance, and most-needed, a friendly smile and welcome. We felt home.

Good neighbors and friends. This book is going to tell you a lot about the people who have helped us over the last few years, so I don't want to get ahead of myself. But I must tell you that friends and neighbors are as much a part of the farm as, say, the barn or the hayfield or the fencing. I feel on quite solid ground to state that without them, we would be in a mess.

If you have never started a totally new direction in your life, like living on a farm, you may be wondering what kinds of things friends and neighbors do to help. People have taught us how to grow plants in this clay soil, how to buy farm equipment, what to look for when buying horses, how to tell when a cow is about to give birth, how to butcher, who to contact for more information, how to interact with farmers and people in this area, which stores to patronize and which to avoid, how to bid at an auction, and how to keep things from freezing in our minus 40 degree winters. They have shared their plants, animals, books, tools, equipment, trucks, cars, trailers, skills, and time. They have answered 1001 questions at all times of the day and night (like, "The horse just won't stand still to be groomed. What should we do?"). They have come over to our farm to personally walk-us-through many a new task (like milking a cow). They brought us meals and flowers, grieving with us when we lost an unborn baby. In short, they have been neighbors and friends. The kind you read about in old books. The kind you thought were no longer around. Well, they are around.

My advice is to choose a farm near people who can be good neighbors and friends. How do you find such a place? Based just on my experience I'm afraid I couldn't give you much of a clue. Because that is not what we actively tried to do. We were just trying to find a great farm to live on. Thankfully, it does seem as though there are many people like these living in the country. We asked God to help us find the best area to live in, and we know He blessed that request.

Everyone here is so friendly and interested in what we're doing. Sandy Tyykila, the postmaster, asked me the very first time I walked into the post office, "Oh, you must be the Castleberrys. You bought the old Ahola place, didn't you? I hear you have five children. How old are they?" When Susie was checking out at the Poplar Hardware store right after we moved in, she asked where Maple was. Pastor Dan Erickson was standing there and said, "If you don't know where Maple is, you sure must be new to town!" He and his lovely wife Nancy have been helpful in giving directions (both geographic and spiritual) since that time. Lu Harnstrom and Alice Christensen at the Poplar Hardware Hank store always ask about the newest baby and let us weigh it on their nail scale. Steve Kapsalis, known in our family as "Steve at the dump," happily greets us each time we take our trash to the township dumpster, no matter if the weather is 30° below zero or 100° above. It would be impossible for me to mention all of the helpful, friendly people we interact with in this neighborhood and in Poplar. The crazy thing is that years ago, in our suburban lifestyle, we would probably have viewed much of this as just people being "nosy." In reality it is true friendly interest, and the people here really care about us. That feels good!

Oh, and don't forget. To have good neighbors, you must be good neighbors also. Be willing to offer everything you have to your friends and neighbors. At first, it may seem that you have nothing to offer. But as time goes on, you are able to help, share, teach, and give to those around you. It's a really neat life. I recommend it highly.

Let me introduce a few of my friends right now. Just because these friends are introduced here doesn't mean that our other friends are somehow less than friends. I simply want to provide more background on some of the people who happen to be mentioned often in the rest of this book.

I've already introduced the Bitner clan in the first chapter. Martin is a hardworking first-class dairy farmer, and his wife, Bev, works at the local junior high school. We can see their farm from our house because it is just across the hay fields. Todd Bitner is Martin's son and dairying partner and he lives with his wife Becky in the house next to Martin's. Todd has a crazy sense of humor, and his self-proclaimed goal in life is to have a "push-button" for everything. In addition to putting up with Todd, Becky works at the local elementary school.

The Berthiaumes, Jeff and Sandee, live right across the road from us. Besides dishing out gobs of hospitality and help to people, as I have illustrated in this chapter, Jeff is the most professional and skilled carpenter/cabinet maker I have ever met. Sandee, in addition to raising their three beautiful daughters, is always busy doing things to help others less blessed than herself in the community. Although they own a lot of land, Jeff and Sandee don't really have a farm and don't have any animals. Which is why I wasn't thrilled with the behavior of our cows in their driveway!

Robin Berglund will be mentioned a lot in this book. He is one of the smartest, most creative, capable, helpful people I have ever met in all my life. He has a college education (including an array of bachelor and master degrees), but it is what he has taught himself that amazes me. He has taught college courses in math, is a professional computer systems analyst and programmer, and can build or do anything that needs to be done. The only thing he doesn't do for himself is work on his own teeth. I expect that he will tackle that some day soon! His wife Marlene is his wonderful helpmate and supporter. Both have meant so much to us.

Finally, I will mention Uncle Jim and Aunt Marie Baumann. They are affectionately called "uncle" and "aunt" by my children because they are just like family. Jim works for the U. S. Justice Department and, like me, owns a "hobby farm" that consumes a lot of his off-time. Jim is a hardworking man who will do anything to help a friend. Marie, like Jim, has taught us so much about living on a farm because she has experienced just about everything (raising chickens and turkeys, butchering, grinding grain for flour, milking goats, cooking on a woodstove, buying from cooperatives, etc.).

It may seem like all of our friends have a last name that starts with "B." That is not true, but it is amazing how many do start with "B." There are two sets of Bitners, Berthiaumes, two sets of Berglunds, Baumanns, Beckels, Bentons, etc. At first, it was very confusing to us, but we about have it all worked out now.

In terms of the layout of our farm, by far the most prominent building is the big red barn. It was built in 1929 by an American who was "bound and determined to show these immigrants (our area is full of Finnish and Swedish descendants) how farming should be done." I understand that it bankrupted him. But at least it was well built. It is 101 feet long, 38 feet wide, and more than 60 feet tall (that's tall!). A neighbor told us he remembers putting more than 10,000 bales of hay in it one summer. It is in good shape except for windows which seem to endlessly need repairing and replacing. Several outbuildings were also here when we moved in: a 25' x 27' two-car garage, a 12' x 27' one-car garage which was moved in and served as a sort of shop, an old 16' x 12' milk cooling house, and a small 5' x 8' hen house. There was also the small (the tax rolls called it a "bungalow") farmhouse of about 1056 square feet which was supposed to house my crew of seven.

Our farm is located in Lakeside, a beautiful, quiet township which 564 people call "home." It sports three major rivers as well as many creeks and streams that flow directly into Lake Superior. The township has no bank, no grocery store, no gas station, not even a tiny convenience store. In fact, there are no retail businesses I am aware of (except for the usual small out-of-your-house businesses like taxidermist, beautician, deer processor, etc.). A few people dairy farm or raise beef "in a big way" but almost every family has one member who also works in one of the bigger towns close by. There are lots of people like us who cut hay and raise some animals but aren't full time farmers. The clay soil around here simply isn't rich enough nor the growing season long enough (or predictable enough) to support much else.

Now that you know how we got started and what our farm and township are like, let me start telling you about some of the things we have learned. In the next chapter I'll give you a glimpse of what it is like to live with laying hens on the place.

Chapter 3
Laying Hens Can Be Lots Of Fun

The house was still very much under construction, the barn was still a wreck, the temperature was high, and I'm afraid my patience was quite slim when Susie brought up the subject of layers. "Why don't we get some laying hens?" she asked. "It sure would be nice to have fresh eggs. Besides, we need to get them now so they can begin growing. It takes five months before we actually get eggs from them!"

"I'm not sure I'm ready for anything more right now," I replied.

But after more discussion, it was agreed that layers were just what we needed. We ordered the chicks. We get ours from Utgaards Hatchery in Star Prairie, WI because they ship directly to our feed store. There are lots of kinds of laying chickens to choose from. If we want white egg layers, we can choose from White Leghorns, California Whites, DeKalp, Babcock, or Hy-Line. For brown egg layers the choices are Rhode Island Reds, Hisex Browns, Arbor Acre Browns, Barred Rock, Black Austalorps, White Rocks, or Black Sex Links. Whew! What a lot to choose from! Especially for someone who thought a chicken was just a chicken. Barred Rock ended up being our choice because we wanted an old-fashioned breed that laid brown eggs. We liked the fact that Barred Rock is also a meat-type bird, a handy feature as they get older (or if you have a really mean chicken).

Of course before they came, we had to clean out the hen house, fix the broken windows and make them operable, and fix the door. I remember thinking that cleaning out the old dried-up chicken manure was a smelly, not wholly satisfying job. "But at least when this is done it will be done," I said to myself with some sense of relief. "Then they'll have a clean place to live and I won't have to do this again." That kind of thinking is just like when Jeannie, our first baby, started teething. Since she was in such pain, I rushed out to the grocery store to buy some teething gel to relieve her suffering, but was disgusted to see that the smallest size tube for sale was pretty large. "Oh, well," I thought, "maybe we will be able to use it all up eventually!" How little did I know! What I should have done was buy it by the case, or perhaps even a full carload. She didn't stop teething, the pain came back with *each* tooth, and I kept going back to the store time and time again to get more teething gel.

Well, guess what? When you clean out the manure it won't be long before it should be cleaned out again. Why that was so hard for me to fathom, I don't know. Maybe it's because I wasn't born on a farm. Maybe it is because I wanted to think that I could get a job completely done and behind me. I can think of almost nothing on a farm which you do once, then never have to do again. In fact that is one of the hardest lessons I have had to learn. It is never done. Everything is done over and over again. There is a pattern and rhythm to it all: clean out the hen house, feed and water the chickens daily, a few months later clean out the hen house, feed and water the chickens daily . . . You get the idea.   You either get used to this pattern, or you are going to be one unhappy homesteader! Actually, the steady rhythm of doing chores sequentially, over and over, can be quite fulfilling. You get the feeling that you're doing something really worthwhile (as opposed to, say, watching reruns on TV for the tenth time--we have no TV, so I no longer know what this is like).

Finally, the eight Barred Rock chicks arrived (along with our meat birds and a few turkeys-more about them later). Of course, I wasn't home when they made their grand and noisy arrival at the feed store. Phyllis Massier, our indispensable feed store manager, called and said, "Mrs. Castleberry, your chicks are here. It's really cold and you probably should come get them quickly." We only had one car at the time and I had it at work. Susie called Lil Faugerstrom (Anderson), affectionately called "Cookie" (she turned 80 a few years ago), who drove her to the store and picked them up. I suppose I should also mention that it was pouring down rain, it was about 50° outside (chicks are supposed to stay warm-like 90°!), and Susie and Cookie also had to bring home bags of feed and grit along with the chickens. Cookie had raised many a chick in her life, and it didn't bother her at all. It was one miserable trip I was spared. I will be forever grateful for Cookie's willingness to help us out that day.

Because of the rainy, cold weather, the children were unable to go out to see the new chicks that morning. They were so disappointed that Susie got an old bathtowel and sloshed back through the ankle-deep water in front of the chick house. Carefully wrapping up a fluffy chick, she carried it back to the kitchen, where the children crowded all around her, oohing and aahing over it. Baby chicks really are cute.

When I got home from work, I strolled out to look at our new charges. My heart melted a little when I saw those fuzzy little one day-old Barred Rock fluff balls. They were so cute! The neatest thing was the way they would stand on top of the paper plates of feed, and with head poised high, scratch for the food. It was like they were walking backwards and scratching at the same time: scratch, scratch, scratch (those who are sharp in physics will realize that the chicks are now three steps back of where they started), then beak down and eat the food. The funniest thing is that they had no need to scratch! The food was just lying there. But all of that scratching around is actually a good instinct and serves them well when they scratch for bugs later in their lives.

Stevie, then only eight years old, was heart-broken a few days later when he found our first casualty. He came running to the house with a tear-streaked face, holding a limp little fluffy body. He, as well as the other children, soon adjusted to the hard fact of death, however, and have not had any real problems since.

During that first week it didn't seem to me like they were eating enough food. Ever see a new mother worry about how much food her baby eats? The mother frets and talks about how "little Jimmy" just doesn't eat much and she worries so! Then one day you get a look at "little Jimmy" and see that he is one of the healthiest babies you have ever seen. Well, that was the same deal with these new chicks and me. Were they healthy? Of course they were. They grew and grew and grew and soon I was putting up a roosting bar for them to roost on, and a laying box for them to lay in.

Okay, education time. Do you need a rooster to get eggs? No. I must admit I didn't know this and found it hard to believe. But it's true. Just think about other animals which go through an egg cycle every month or so and you will probably catch on. Chickens go through an "egg cycle" every day or so.

Speaking of eggs. Ever had a real egg? I mean a *really* fresh egg? I hadn't. They have flavor. They're large and the yolk is large. They also seemed special to us since they were brown. These eggs are so fresh that it's best to wait three days before attempting to make hard-boiled eggs. You can still boil brand new eggs; it just takes 20 minutes for a hard-boiled egg. It's difficult to find anything similar between home-raised eggs and store-bought eggs.

It's fun to watch a hen lay an egg. Whoever said, "A chicken won't let you watch her lay an egg," never met our hens. Everyone in our family has seen our chickens lay eggs. Once she starts laying she can't stop even if you're looking. Sometimes you can hear them grunt right when they lay. When the egg first comes out it is wet (this is called the bloom), but it soon dries off. It's warm too, and stays warm as long as mama sits on it.

After a year, the chickens start to molt. That means they lose their feathers and look more like Phyllis Diller than anything else. They also stop laying during this time, which lasts about two months. Some people kill them and put them in the stew pot, rather than feed them with no immediate returns (eggs). We chose to keep our first batch of laying chickens. In fact, we were so pleased with our egg-laying crew that we decided to invest more energy and money into them.

I got ambitious and built them their own enclosed chicken area inside the barn. Most books I've read said you need about four square feet of floor space per layer. We made ours 13 feet by 13 feet, which is quite a bit larger than suggested. I have since learned that you really don't have to, and sometimes should not, go by suggestions found in books. Usually, they are written for someone who wants to maximize production in the smallest space possible. I have also since read that hens will do much better if they have a lot of room to move around in, and you won't have to clean out their area so often.

I also built them five laying boxes with each one about two feet wide and one foot high. The sides only go half-way up so the chickens can "talk" to each other as they lay. At least the books I read said the layers would like to sit in separate boxes and talk to each other. Actually, we have found that our chickens like to lay eggs in the same box pretty much. Sometimes there will even be two hens in one box laying eggs at the same time. The laying boxes have a walkway in front (theoretically so the chickens can walk up and down and check out all the available real estate before choosing one to build a nest in), and have a hinged door in the back so that the little children can check for eggs without even going into the chicken coop area. We have a glove there for the children to use because a hen sitting on eggs can peck you if you try to steal her eggs.

I also built a small twelve inch square doorway so the hens could walk out of the barn during the day. This turned out to be one of the hardest parts of the job because our barn has several layers of interior and exterior walls with air spaces. Finally, I put up two roosting bars and staggered them so that the hens on top can't mess up the hens using the lower bar. But of course, they all crowd together on the top bar.

The laying chickens now had what I considered a palace to live in. What more could they want?

Well, how about something to protect them from the wild animals? Up here where we live, we have quite a number of animals that would just love to eat very fresh chicken or good, fresh eggs (didn't I tell you the eggs were great?). We have raccoons, skunks, coyotes, foxes, wolves, bears, bobcats, minks, fishers, badgers, weasels, hawks, eagles, rats, and the usual array of local farm dogs and cats that sometimes roam at night. How do I know they like chicken? Personal experience.

It was 6:00 a.m. when I heard a commotion outside my bedroom window. Sounded like a dump truck must be running over the chickens, then backing up, and running over the chickens again and again. All the chickens were squawking and making the worst racket. So, I did what every farmer would do. I closed the window and put a pillow over my head. Naw, I jumped up, mumbled something intelligent to Susie like "They are eating . . . are my pants? . . . I can't find . . ." and then disappeared down the stairs two at a time. As I passed through the living room heading for the gun cabinet, I saw Jeannie and Stevie quietly reading books like nothing was happening. I grabbed my .410 shotgun and headed for the chickens. When I got to the back of the chicken coop, there was a chicken lying on the ground acting rather strangely. It had one leg under the chicken coop and its body was banging, banging up against the bottom sill of the coop. I realized that something was trying to drag one of my egg-laying wonders under the coop in order to do unkind things to it.

I got angry. Being a man of action, I grabbed the chicken's other leg and started trying to pull it away from the bandit. We had quite a tug of war for about 15 seconds. The hen was not having fun, I could tell. "Gotta be a pretty big, strong animal under there," I thought. Finally I pulled just as hard as I could and I won--the chicken was in my clutches alone. But it was a really bloody mess and I knew that it wasn't going to live. So I laid the hen in the middle of the hen yard, stepped back a few steps, picked up the shotgun, and waited for the varmint to appear.

I didn't have to wait long. First, its head came out. It looked at me. It looked at the chicken. It looked at me again. Whoosh . . . it rushed out to grab the chicken. Dumb decision. I successfully ended the assault with a single shot.

"Now why am I shaking all over?" I wondered. I had never shot an animal that I could remember and it was not an easy thing to do. Also, my adrenalin must have been at an all time high. It's probably a pretty hard thing on your body to go from deep sleep to maximum adrenalin instantly. I now have more respect for firefighters who do it all the time. Besides, I didn't really want to kill that animal. After all, it just wanted to eat my chicken. But we couldn't let it eat our egg-laying marvels. Needless to say, I was a something of a hero in my house that morning.

Okay, so we need some protection. What to get? Llamas, donkeys, geese, guinea hens, and dogs are all supposed to be good watch animals. I made my decision after considering all of the facts. Fact one: dogs are free, everything else costs. End of facts. We got a dog. Actually, we got two of them because we had heard that two dogs are better than one. With two dogs you get better protection: one dog could always stay and guard the farm animals and the other one can guard the children as they play in the fields and woods. Also, when someone knows you have <u>dogs</u> (instead of just one dog) they are more cautious and might not be as likely to invade your private property and steal your tractor that won't start!

We heard about someone whose full-blooded German Shepherd dog had just had puppies and gave them a call. They were only too thrilled to give us two cute jet-black Shepherd/Lab puppies. Since they were sisters (the puppies, not the owners), we reasoned, they would play well together and probably be happier. Boy, were we right. They played together a lot. The children played with the puppies a lot too. But the puppies played together more often. In fact, they started acting just the least little bit like a pack of wild dogs (the puppies again, not my children). As they grew bigger, they grew stronger. We could see that we were going to have two huge dogs on our hands. But, that's no problem. Remember. We got them to protect the chickens. The bigger the better I say.

"Daddy, oh Daddy, oh Daddy! They've killed the chickens and now you're going to kill them! Oh Daddy, oh Daddy!" wailed six-year-old Katie, running to the house breathlessly, her face tear-streaked. What would be your first reaction? Would you be calm? Would you reach for your pipe and slowly fill it, then cradling the child on your knee ask, "Now why don't you just slowly tell me what happened, from the beginning?" Not me. Not owning a pipe, I ran pell-mell out of the house to see for myself what she was talking about. I found the dogs and they sure weren't the things Katie was trying to tell me about being dead. Then I found the chickens. All over the place. The dogs had chased them and broken most of their necks. Great chicken-guard dogs! Then it dawned on me that these were Shepherd/Lab dogs. Labs. You know, the breed of dogs that are known as some of the best BIRD dogs! I scolded the dogs and did what I had read in dog training books (hit the dog in the face with the dead animal that you want them not to go after again). That was hard! As soon as I let them loose, they wandered back to the chickens to try and finish them off. Every chance they got, they went back again. In the end, we had to get rid of both dogs and the remaining crippled chickens. That wasn't fun either!

Living in the country is never dull. Sometimes you get a phone call that can change the plans for your day (or year) completely! For example, one day not long after we lost all of our hens, we got a most interesting call from a friend whom I'll call Beth. Beth said she knew a family who had 25 older laying hens that they didn't want anymore. Although these hens were over a year old, they were still laying eggs occasionally (one a piece every few days or so). "Why do they want to get rid of them?"

I'm generally a cautious person and when someone says "free" I start asking questions. It's like the time we got a "free" Thanksgiving turkey from the grocery store. All we had to do was buy so many dollars worth of groceries, which we did, and we got this great big free turkey. The fact that it was some "off-brand" didn't concern me when I picked it up. A turkey was a turkey, right? On Thanksgiving morning Susie started cooking that bird, and boy, the house started stinking like all get out! We tossed the turkey out the back door, and I ended up driving all over town trying to find a replacement. There was not a single turkey to be found anywhere. So, I brought home a puny little hen instead. No, I don't just automatically take something that is free anymore.

"Why don't they just kill the chickens and put them in the stew pot?" we asked Beth. "Because they don't have the heart to kill them," Beth replied. "They have become just like pets. They don't mind someone else killing them, they just can't do it themselves," Beth added.   After talking it over, we gave the family a call and said that sure, we would love to have 25 free hens.

Now, the big question was how to bring them home. Remember that hens are quite noisy, fluttery animals that like to mess things up. I could just hear one of the hens saying to her friend as they sat in my van, "Hey! Cloth seats! Let's mess them up!" I wasn't about to let them have their little fling, however. We considered putting them in cardboard boxes or caging off the back of the van ("Hey! Carpet! Let's mess it up!").   Why not just throw them all in the little open-top trailer we owned, toss a piece of cardboard on top and drive them home? Since we couldn't think of a better solution, that is just what we did.

Susie's parents were visiting us at the time and we casually told them we were going to go pick up some free laying hens and would be back soon. They weren't raised on a farm, either, and sort of gave us a queer look, like "Wouldn't it just be easier to buy eggs at the store?" No, they didn't want to ride along for the fun, but thanks anyway.

When we arrived at the friend of our friend's farm, we found the father back by the hen house and a little boy sniffling, looking like he was going to burst into tears at any minute. He sure was unhappy to see those hens leave. Sort of made me feel like I was stealing candy from a baby. But the parents knew this was the best way to handle the situation, so we proceeded. Now, wouldn't you think that those hens would just love to see us, fly into our trailer, line up quietly, and wait for us to put a piece of cardboard over their heads? Me too! But they didn't. Some took off for the woods and we never did find them. Others hid in the dark hen house trying to blend in with the woodwork. The ones we put in the trailer just flew back out. So we had to put the cardboard over the trailer top, quickly open it for the father to toss in a hen, then quickly shut it to keep the rest from flying out. Chickens were squawking, perspiration was flying, and the little boy was sobbing. A lot of fun, you might say. Finally, after capturing all we could find, we thanked the people and drove out of the driveway.

We had eight miles to drive home and I was in no hurry. I had children stationed in the back of the van, keeping watch over the cardboard. My fear was that the cardboard would fly off. Can you imagine what that would mean? It would mean 25 wild chickens flying and running away from my van as fast as they could. And it could also mean chickens flying into passing cars' windshields causing wrecks and general havoc. No sir, I was determined to drive slowly and be sure that I didn't have to put on my brakes too quickly. Everything was going well until a shaggy black bear jumped out of the ditch and walked right in the front of the car. Imagine 25 chickens running around with a big black bear tearing them up, children crying, and someone saying he just had to go the bathroom right now! Thankfully it didn't happen. We missed the bear, the cardboard stayed on, and we got home with no other problems. I feel God blessed us on that trip!

When we got home, we had to try to figure out how to unload them from the trailer into the hen house. We thought of all sorts of ways to do it. Finally, we just opened the back of the trailer and let them fly/jump out. These were pretty wild birds of every imaginable size and breed. In addition to some of the breeds I mentioned earlier, we had one or more of several exotic varieties like Golden Sebright Bantams, Silver-Gray Dorkings, Buff Orpingtons, and Mille Fleur Booted Bantams. We even had some strange looking Houdans with long feathers on top of their heads that are shaped like a spewing water fountain at the mall. Looked like a circus instead of a farm. The children loved it!

Most of the hens flew far up into the tree tops to roost that night. Kind of made us wonder where we were supposed to look for the eggs they would deposit. Should I use my 24-foot ladder and check the lower branches?

After a few days, we realized that we weren't really going to need all of these hens. Some weren't laying and we didn't need any stewing birds. So four days later we called a few friends and they came and took some home. One family even "showed" some of the exotic birds at the county fair. That is what country life is all about. Sharing with others. It's fun.

We kept eight of these free hens for ourselves, but our local racoons decided that they just had to have a little taste of fresh chicken and had plans of their own. Every night they would get into the hen house and eat a hen. I would wake up and hear a sudden SQUAWK, look at Susie and sadly/madly say "Those lousy 'coons got another one! WHO LEFT THE HEN HOUSE DOOR OPEN AGAIN?" Then one evening, I closed up the hen house myself. Those hens were snug as a bug in a rug. That night we heard another hen becoming supper for a 'coon. I finally realized that those smart 'coons were unlatching the hook to the hen's private entrance (the door through which they exited to soak up a few rays of sunshine each day) and just walking (or probably strutting) in. To fix that I replaced the hook and eye closure which was on the outside of the hen house with a barrel bolt that I placed on the inside of the hen house. That made it a little harder to close the hens up at night, but it was sure effective at stopping the raccoons.

Finally we were down to four hens, getting only one or two eggs a day. That wasn't enough for us. What to do now? Buy more chickens. And don't get any more dogs. Good plan. We got 25 hens this time because we decided that we would like to sell eggs. Sounds old fashioned and neat, doesn't it? A scene that Norman Rockwell would want to paint, with a little hand-painted sign by the road that says "Eggs for Sale." As it turned out, we didn't need any sign by the road. People were lined up to buy our eggs!

After the 25 pullets arrived, we noticed that one of them was getting bigger faster than the others. All hens grow a funny thing on the top of their head (called a comb), but this one's comb was a bit larger than the other hens'. "That's a rooster," I said.

"No, that is just a hen that is more mature. I'm sure she'll lay the first egg," Susie said confidently. As time went on, the children and I were pretty sure it was a rooster, but Susie was insistent. "Just watch. She'll lay the first egg." Then one morning Jeannie and Stevie ran into the house laughing. "Hey

Mommy? Remember that hen that was going to lay the first egg?" "Yes?" asked Susie, smiling expectantly. The children shouted in unison, "Well, she CROWED this morning!"

So, what to do with a rooster? Why not try to raise some chicks ourselves? Yeah, why pay 69 cents apiece for something we could do ourselves!?! You know, cut out the middle man, so to speak. What do you need? Fertile eggs. Okay, we have a rooster for that, so no problem there.

Well, actually we did have a problem there. You see, our rooster was one of those Chicago gangster kind of roosters. He loved to inflict pain and let everyone know he was the boss. He was generally mean to the hens and would peck them unmercifully. When Stevie would go into the coop to do the chores, the rooster would shake all his feathers and run at Stevie with his wings hanging down. He pecked several of the children pretty hard. It finally got to the point where no one wanted to go into the chicken coop anymore. The only solution was to get rid of the rooster. A Daddy job.

Okay, the trouble maker was now history (and great with dumplings), but we had our hopes set on raising our own chicks, so what could we do? When our good friends, Mark and Denise Beckel, learned of our interests, they graciously gave us a very well-mannered rooster. In fact, this rooster was actually afraid of people. What would we do without friends?

But there is one other thing you need to raise your own chicks- a broody hen. That means one that *wants* to sit on a nest. Most hens don't want to just sit on a nest all day (would you?). As it turns out, we had two broody hens. We started gathering eggs and putting them under the broody hens. They were more than happy to oblige. It is important to note that allowing hens to be broody results in a sort of liability because they don't lay any eggs once they start sitting on a nest. Thus, we were taking something of a gamble trying to raise our own chicks. We could have, instead, sold the eggs that the broodies would have laid, and with the money bought day-old chicks.

To their credit, it should be noted that broody hens don't exactly live a life of luxury during their non-egg laying period.

They really have to endure a lot of hardship for their brood. Because they can't get off the nest for very long at a time, broody hens have very few chances to eat or even drink water. In fact, they lose a lot of weight as a result of sitting. They also can't groom themselves as much or take time for a refreshing dust bath. This results in insect infestation. It also leaves them with a very foul odor, even using "chicken standards" with regard to odor. Also, the broody hens have to turn the eggs several times each day. I just wanted to set the record straight so you didn't think it was all rosy being a broody hen (although it's not exactly like any of my readers are going to have the opportunity to become a broody hen themselves).

One day we were walking along the edge of the hay field and spotted a hen sitting on the ground in a very odd way. What made it odd? She didn't want to move. When she did move, under much protest, we discovered twenty-one eggs! We decided to add these to the stock that our broody hens were sitting on. But first we wanted to know if they were fertile eggs with little chicks inside. The proper procedure for doing this is called "candling," which simply means you put the egg over a very bright candling light so you can see what is under the shell. Well, I didn't own a candling light and didn't know anyone else who had one. Do you? Using my slowly-developing farmer ingenuity I placed each egg in front of the bright lights on my van and looked at them closely.

After rejecting one as nonfertile, I would hand it to one of my children. They would then conduct the second test which consisted of throwing them, breaking open the egg, and looking inside. If they found a chick then we knew the egg was fertile. It's kind of like being in the army and testing each of your missiles and rockets to see if they will explode. The good thing is that you will know with complete assurance if they were good; the bad thing is that you no longer have a missile. The end result of our testing, including both sets of tests, is that none of the eggs were fertile. The other result is that I came very close to having a migraine headache from staring at the car's headlights from about three inches away for five minutes.

Meanwhile, the two broody hens were sitting on their nest of eggs doing what they were supposed to be doing, ignoring our antics. In our eager desire to hatch home-raised chicks, we had more than twenty eggs under each hen. We have since learned that is too many eggs for them to sit on - twelve is closer to the optimum number.

It takes 21 days to hatch an egg. After a couple of weeks, however, one hen had had enough fun and went on strike (meaning she simply walked away from the nest). That left one hen upon whom we rested all our hopes. Don't feel any pressure or anything like that! Oh, and we put the eggs from the striking broody hen under the remaining hen. She had, shall we say, a "full house!"

Days went by slowly while the smell increased exponentially. Each day we would find more broken eggs under her. She simply had too many eggs to sit on. Finally, one glorious day we walked into the hen house and found a single tiny black baby chick under her wing. Two changes in the hen occurred instantly. First, she got off her nest and refused to bring the rest of her brood into this world. For those of you keeping a financial scorecard on this episode, you have probably figured out that we are losing our shirts on this deal. Second, her personality changed. She went from not-the-nicest-hen-in-the-world to one-of-the-meanest-hens-in-the-world. I don't blame her. She was just being an old mother hen, and she displayed all the traits of some mother you have probably thought of in your mind as an "old mother hen." When someone would come into the hen house, she would puff out her wings and hide her chick inside her feathers. She would also cluck and cluck and cluck, as if to say "Out of here, you worthless creature! You are not wanted here! Shoo, human!" I will have to say to her credit that she was a good mother. It was fun to watch the hen teach her little chick how to scratch and find bugs. She was very protective and we have her chick (now a grown hen) to this day.

We have tried to brood our own chicks a couple of other times since then, never with any success. We are thinking of building an incubator and trying it that way. Then, all of the work of the hen (keeping them at 99.5° and moist, turning them three times a day) becomes our responsibility. One advantage, though, is that it should be much less smelly!

As mentioned earlier, we have to feed and water the chickens daily. While that's not a particularly difficult job, it has required some modification over the years. We started out feeding the chickens using a special feeder with a smooth dowel mounted loosely on top. The theory is that when chickens try to roost on that dowel, it will spin, causing them to fall off, which will prevent them from dropping manure in their feed. It didn't work for us, although I'm not sure why. Maybe our chickens had special talents for hanging onto spinning dowels! Anyway, I then made some simple wooden feeders with a solid panel on top. They would roost on top, but their manure couldn't get into the feed. But the mice could. They kept getting in and eating that expensive chicken feed. Then I read about a hanging feeder and made one. It was just a hanging bucket with slits near the bottom and a large pan screwed to the bottom. As the chickens ate grain, more would come sliding out of the slits into the pan. That didn't work either, because too much grain came out of the slits, spilling onto the floor. I finally built a large wooden feeder that would hold plenty of grain but then we started having rats. To solve that I put a wooden cover on top of the feed at night. Those rats were not discouraged, though, and simply chewed a large hole in the bottom of the wooden feeder and ate all the grain they wanted. My solution was to get some poison, place it where only the rats could reach it, and kill the rats. A very effective solution I might add. Now, our only thieves of the chicken feed are small birds which find their way into the chicken coop.

We keep the bulk of our feed for each animal in metal garbage cans with tight fitting lids. No animals have ever molested those large garbage cans, probably because they can't smell what's inside.

We provided water for our chickens using one-gallon plastic waterers. These are good except that they freeze and break in the winter. They also need to be filled pretty often. As a solution we bought five gallon metal waterers. These work great in the summer but freeze in the winter. Chickens drink less in winter than during the warm summer months, however, so we just fill a 9" x 13" cake pan or old bread pan with water. When it freezes solid, we simply turn it over, tap it on the concrete floor, and all the ice falls out. An easy, cheap solution!

People who keep chickens for eggs want to get those eggs, and not share them with predators or lose them by having a chicken build a nest in some hidden place. We have done several things to help insure we get the eggs. We don't let the chickens out of their coop until after lunch. Most lay in the morning, and hence, into our nesting boxes under this plan. We have had several hens that got a taste for eating fresh eggs. They weren't hard to spot because they had egg yolk smeared on their beaks! To try to break them of this habit, we would isolate the guilty hens and provide them with an egg to eat that was laced with cayenne pepper. The theory states that the hen will take one bite, then run to the waterer and never even think of eating another egg. Not so for our hens. In fact, they seemed to enjoy the pepper. I could almost hear my hen saying, "Wouldn't have a bit of salt too, would you bub?" We finally had to kill the egg eaters. We wanted to be the egg eaters.

We also had a desire to sell our fresh eggs to others. As a marketing professor, I tapped into all of my marketing expertise for this enterprise. What was my magnificent strategic marketing plan? I asked Susie who would like to buy some eggs. When she asked our neighbors and friends, they all said "yes" plus we got some referral business. We actually had one customer, Roberta Grube, who agreed to buy any and all extra eggs we had.   We sold our eggs for $1.00 a dozen, which is a price that everyone seems to use. That is a very fair price for a dozen eggs. So, how can grocery stores offer eggs on sale for 29 cents a dozen, or some such ridiculous price? Simple. They lose money on every dozen they sell, but they know they will make it up with the profits they make on all the other items you buy while you are getting the cheap eggs. The same is true of many sales on meat, fruits, and vegetables. While this is all well and good for the consumer who just wants to save the most money he can, it makes it very hard for a local farmer to make a living selling fresh local produce. Think about it.

I kept very careful records of my expenses in this egg business. I knew what our feed and grit bill was. When I subtracted this amount from my egg sales, I only saw negative numbers. What this means is that I lost money selling eggs. A lot? No. But do I want to keep losing money? Why not get 250 laying hens and lose a bundle?!? Although that is the way our government seems to be run at times, that's not exactly what I understand they teach you at the Harvard Business School. In all fairness, it should be noted that part of our high cost of feed that winter was probably due to the fact that we were experiencing 30 degrees-below-zero kind of weather. We also wanted to take into account our desire to supply good, healthy food for our friends who were unable, for whatever reason, to raise their own chickens for eggs.

Finally, we decided to disband our little business venture, but to sell extra eggs when we have them. To be honest, our children miss selling eggs. They liked calling customers and telling them we had eggs. They also loved talking to the customers when they came to pick up the eggs and tell them everything that was happening on the farm. Who knows, maybe we will start selling eggs again someday, but I hope it will be for more than $1.00 a dozen!

Chapter 4
Our Very Own Garden and Orchard

Onion lovers who enjoy a thick slice of mild, juicy, crisp onion on their hamburger won't want to miss out on these mild giants."

"Fresh, juicy, sweet home-grown melons capture the taste of summer. Best of the acclaimed French Charentais melons, this Honey Girl hybrid is the finest melon you'll ever taste."

"Garden-fresh sweet corn is the summer's greatest pleasure. This hybrid is twice as sweet as ordinary yellow sweet corn and retains its sweetness much longer after being picked!"

"Outstanding disease resistance and hybrid vigor make this tomato stand out in the crowd!"

At least that is what seed catalogs like Burpee's and Jung's promise. Of course, for all of that to happen you have to plant the seeds, and for that you need a garden. Thus began our "search" for our very own garden.

The previous owners had a small garden plot about 8 feet by 15 feet. However, when we moved in, the contractors had filled this area with all of the construction debris. So where I was supposed to harvest succulent red tomatoes, we had a harvest of rotting wood and shingles instead. Besides, we wanted a really big garden spot and 8 x 15 just didn't seem to measure up.

Let's see. First, the ideal garden should have excellent drainage and be south sloping (to capture the early spring rays). Second, it should also be fairly close to the house, so it's not such a big deal to walk out there for a few minutes and weed, water, or harvest some lettuce. Finally, it should consist of a good rich loam soil. Our first garden spot, the old calf-pen area, had two out of three of these traits. It was fenced in and was 40 feet x 120 feet. It was facing south and should drain fairly well due to the slope of the land. Also, it was only about 210 feet from the house. Everything was looking up except for the final ingredient--the soil. It stunk. Pure hardpan red clay dirt.

I was once hired as a consultant to the Soil Conservation Service (SCS) to teach their employees how to "sell" soil conservation to farmers and land owners. As I prepared for my session I read a lot of SCS literature and talked to a number of SCS people. One thing I learned quickly was that you never call the substance on the ground "dirt." Because of its importance (and the necessity of all those SCS jobs) it should be referred to as "soil." Well, with all due respect to the SCS, my farm is nothing but red clay dirt (but I'll try to remember to call it soil in the rest of this book).

If you have never worked in clay soil, you don't know what you're missing. When it rains, the water just lies on top of the soil, making the entire area look like a temporary lake. After the water soaks in, the ground is so clumpy and heavy that it is almost impossible to plow or dig. Just the other day I saw a huge bulldozer oozed down deep in pure red clay, stuck for eternity unless something really big and powerful comes and pulls it out. At the other end of the spectrum, when drought-like conditions occur, the ground splits open and huge cracks/small canyons are created. The dry clay is just like concrete. I have been known to dig dry, red clay for hours just trying to open a hole big enough to put a mailbox post in the ground. (Hint: the secret is to first pour a bucket of water on the soil to loosen it up a bit. Then wait about 30 minutes before digging.) The only good thing about clay is that it does hold moisture. This can come in handy if you get a lot of rain followed by a long dry spell.

Needless to say, I wanted to replace the red clay soil in the garden with rich, black loam soil, just like the soil we had in our little garden at the rental place in Illinois. Assuming we want this good soil to be three feet deep, that would require us to buy about

533 cubic yards of soil at $10.50 per yard. That comes to around $5600! The next best thing is to "spruce up" your poor soil by adding natural nutrients and organic matter. Another word for that is manure. We had three or four good size piles of aged cow manure in the pasture. I didn't feel like moving all of that stuff with my small wheelbarrow, but I did move quite a few loads. It was about 325 feet one way. Actually, 131 steps to be exact, unless I spilled the load while crossing the several ditches, which I did about every three loads or so. I could see that this was not the way I wanted to move all that manure.

Ron, the farmer that we bought the farm from, was still busy picking up his stuff and hauling it away after we had moved in. I noticed that he had his tractor still here to load heavy stuff, so I hired him to move some of the manure for me. I don't know what you know about tractors and loaders, but let me go on record here as saying that, for some tasks, they are fantastic. That tractor rolled over to the manure pile and the front-end loader dropped down, scooped up a big "helping," raised the scoop off the ground, rolled to the garden spot and dropped it right where I wanted it. Each scoop with the loader was equal to about four of my wheelbarrow loads. I watched Ron do this for quite some time. There is something very relaxing about watching someone else do a hard chore that you were dreading to do. It is also sort of lazy, but I <u>was</u> busy doing other things that needed doing on the farm. After a bit, Ron asked if that was enough. I said "Sure," thinking that he was mostly doing it as a favor to me and needed to be going now.

Although he had hauled many loads to the garden, it was nowhere near the 533 cubic yards I had earlier estimated I needed. Really, given the volume, it was more like adding a little fertilizer to the area than bringing in new soil. I still had red clay soil, with a little black stuff laying on the very top. I was very thankful for that black stuff, however little it was.

I needed to plow up the entire garden spot so I grabbed my WalMart tiller and headed to the garden. I stayed out there until it was almost pitch black outside. I got very tired as my tines smacked into that hard red clay, but I felt great. I was actually plowing my own farmland and felt like a farmer. I didn't get romantic about it though, like some people write about. You know. People write about grabbing a handful of soil, holding it to their nostrils, wafting in the sweet smell, and dreaming of tall tomato plants. I am too practical and realistic for that, I am afraid. For me, it was a task that needed to be done so I did it. I worked consistently and systematically at plowing that spot. When I finished plowing, several days later, it was as loose as it was going to get. My arms were plenty sore also.

I have learned the value of having a rear-tine tiller versus a front-tine tiller. Mine is a front-tine model, and in hard packed soil it basically acts like a 200-pound Great Dane wanting desperately to run away from the leash you are holding. Your job is to hold that Dane back (which means the tines are digging up the soil and slowly moving forward). With a rear-tine model (they are more expensive, I warn you!) it is more like you are holding the leash of a sleepy, 65 pound Basset hound that just wants to nap. I was at an auction last week, and they were selling a rear-tine tiller. Roberta Edstrom, the half-owner of the tiller (Charlie, her husband, was the other half-owner), was inching over to where the crowd was gathered as the tiller was being sold. "You look like you're about to bid on your own tiller!" I said. "I'm really thinking about it! I love that tiller. It's so easy to use," she replied.

Susie mapped out her garden and ordered her seeds and plants. In addition to the usual vegetables (broccoli, corn, potatoes, carrots, onions, celery, etc.), we also planted blueberry bushes, blackberry bushes, grape vines, strawberry plants, and raspberry bushes. Where I come from, we call that "going whole hog!" As things started growing, we realized how nice it would be to have some mulch around the plants. There were several large round hay bales left behind when Ron moved out. These round bales can easily weigh more than 1000 pounds apiece. Ron probably left them because some of the strings holding them together had broken and moving them would have been a chore with a tractor and wagon. That was no problem for me since I didn't own a single tractor or a wagon. I didn't even own a pickup truck. My solution to moving the bales was simple. I would just load them up in our only car, a full-size, eight passenger van.

The children had a ball. We would drive out to a hay bale and back the van up close. Then, opening up the back doors wide, we would toss loose hay into the interior of the car. We would cram as much in as we could, covering the seats and everything else, and then head to the garden spot. The children would ride in the van with their legs hanging out the big sliding side door. They were really having fun, pretending they were riding on a real hay wagon. The neighbors probably thought we were out of our minds.

But the hay got moved. I only had two concerns. First, I wasn't sure how we were ever going to get the left-behind hay out of the van's nice cloth upholstery and carpet. That ended up being a slow, painstaking task involving the use of vacuum cleaners and whisk brooms, and still leaving some behind. Second, the hay was chock full of little critters called mice and I was afraid one (or more) would decide to take up residence in my van's interior. The children did see a mouse in the van as we were driving to the garden, but thought it must have jumped out at its new home.

Susie fails to see the cuteness in mice. She doesn't even care for Mickey Mouse. I could just picture us heading to church when suddenly a little mouse (or cute little mouse family) decided to make its presence known by running across the floorboard. Thankfully, that never happened. However, when my car was running very poorly later, the mechanic's written comment on the bill read, "Removed rodents' nest from intake manifold, should run better now!" I'm not saying that the mice in the engine were the same ones I saw while we were picking up the hay - but I imagine they were related.

After laying as much hay mulch in the garden rows as we could use, we went ahead and moved the rest of the hay piles just inside the garden fence. This turned out to be a dumb decision because it just molded and started rotting. We were afraid the mold would get all over the plants so we moved it again, this time away from the garden. Also, the hay we used as mulch between plants was responsible for millions of new weeds thanks to the hay seed. So we raked a lot of it away from the plants and hauled it out of the garden too. Seems like that hay was having a very good time moving all over the farm. I would have been smarter to ask others' opinions before putting down hay for mulch.

But isn't that the way we operate so much of the time? We run out and buy something without talking to a good friend first. I'll never forget buying one of those big electric bug zappers when I lived down in Georgia. We had lots of bugs and the advertisements promised that a bug zapper would be the end of those pesky creatures. Well, I bought about the biggest one they sold, brought it home, and read the directions carefully. The manufacturer suggested that I set the zapper up about 20 feet from our deck. The theory is that the zapper will attract all of the bugs in the neighborhood and electrocute them when they touch the metal bug screen on the zapper. Oh, ours zapped bugs all right! The only problem was that the zapper was so good at attracting bugs, and we were right in the line of flight from the field to the zapper. "Smack! Thud! Crash!" Those bugs would fly, full speed, into our faces heading for the zapper. To avoid ending up in the hospital due to bug- impact lacerations, we finally had to unplug the silly thing. I should have checked with some other people before investing in the zapper. Likewise, I should have checked with others before using hay for mulch.

I talked to Robin about the mess of moving hay in my van (you can admit anything to a true friend) and said, "I'll probably have to buy a pickup truck to do stuff like that on the farm." "Do you really want one?" he asked. I confessed that I wouldn't mind having one someday, but didn't want to invest in a truck at the moment. His suggestion was simple: buy a small trailer that can be hooked up to the back of my van. It made so much sense that I wondered why I hadn't thought of it myself! Looking through the paper, I saw a strong, yet light, aluminum trailer for sale for a couple of hundred bucks. I bought it and had a trailer hitch installed on my van for about $125. After getting the trailer lights hooked up, I was out less than $350, and still had a "truck." That little trailer was one of the best investments I have ever made. I can haul just about everything in it. I have hauled hay, firewood, brush, aged manure, rocks, 14 foot gates, wood, trash to the dump, a canoe, and children. Better than a truck, my entire family can come along for the trip since we all fit comfortably inside the van. (Ever see a family all crunched into the cab of a pickup truck? Doesn't look like fun to me!) After hauling stuff, when I no longer need a "pickup," I just unhook the trailer and I am back to my standard van. Nice. Really nice. And the fact that it is aluminum is an added bonus because it won't rust out in our heavy snow area, where tons of salt are spread on the highways each winter.

Even though I had my trailer, watching Ron and my neighbors use their tractors sure gave me an itch to own one of those magnificent tools. Logically, I could justify purchasing one because it was impossible to drag my trailer around the fields with my car if the fields were wet or snow covered. Why, I could even move aged manure directly to my garden myself if I just had a tractor. There are so many things that a tractor can do that I was convinced that I needed one.

I am basically a logical, slow-moving, risk-averse individual. Therefore, I asked my farmer friends what kind of things I should look for in a tractor. Todd suggested several things: a 3-point hitch (because many tools today are made for that kind of a hitch), live hydraulics (so I could add a loader or other tools later), one with at least 30 horsepower (so I could power and pull a hay baler), one with ROPS (roll over protection) would also be nice, and for safety in our hilly area I should only consider one with a wide front (meaning the front wheels are spread out about the same distance as the back wheels, instead of being very close together). A live PTO, meaning the power take off works even if the clutch is depressed, would be nice. For example, if you are haying and get bogged down in some heavy hay, it is nice to be able to put in the clutch, let the baler handle the heavy stuff, and then let out the clutch and continue. He also recommended that I buy a tractor that I could easily get parts for locally. Although you can get parts for just about any brand of tractor anywhere in the world, it may take several days - days that you just don't have during a busy haying season, for example. He suggested that I observe the "blow-by pipe" and see if it is letting out a lot of exhaust. He also happily agreed to look over any tractor that I was thinking about buying and even looked at a few tractors for me at dealers when he was there.

I started watching ads for tractors and suddenly realized that I was totally out of my scope of experience. What is the difference between an Allis-Chalmers 45, a John Deere 3020, a Ford 900, and an International 350? Which is bigger? Which is older? There seemed to be no rhyme or reason to the numbering or lettering of tractor models. How does a Ford 8N compare with a Ford 7710? I had no idea. I checked out a book from the library titled *Encyclopedia of American Farm Tractors* and got some feel for model numbers of the really old tractors. What I learned is that the numbers really do not make any sense and that it was almost impossible to learn something about a tractor just by looking at its number because there were so many options that could be added.

As a result, I ended up just calling the want ad numbers and asking lots of questions. I was surprised to find that many people didn't know the answers to my simple questions. "Does it have live PTO?" I would ask. "Sure, it has a PTO," would be the reply. "Yes, but is it live, does it work when you push in the clutch?" I would query. "Yeah, it has a PTO, like I said," would be the answer. Or I would ask, "How many horsepower does it have?" "I don't know, but you sure can do just about anything with the thing!" would be the response. In fact, I would say that at least 80% of the people I called couldn't tell me, even in ballpark figures, what horsepower their tractor was. I was confused and not a little frustrated.

One day we were driving into town and saw this really cute tractor sitting in a yard. Remember that word "cute." I took down the phone number that was given, because no one was home, and called the owner that night. "It sold today. Sorry," was his answer. "But I do have another one I am restoring that I guess I could sell if you're interested." The next evening, about dark, my family and I were headed to look at this other "cute" tractor. It was still somewhat disassembled but the owner had many nice things to say about it. He had rebuilt many of the parts, sandblasted and painted most of the frame, put on some new parts, etc.

He had it running when I pulled in, which is not what you want. You want to be able to "cold start" it to see how it would start from scratch. He asked me if I wanted to take it for a run, which I did even though it didn't have its seat installed. I was not able to "field test" it, like you are supposed to, because he lived in the city. Instead, I took it for a run around a city block. It seemed to run fine, I trusted the man, so I bought it.

It was an Allis-Chalmers B. It had a wide front, no live PTO, no hydraulics so I could hook up a loader, no 3 point hitch, no ROPS, and the tractor was only around 20 horsepower (meaning I couldn't realistically use it to put up hay). I didn't even look at the blow-by pipe. I didn't have a clue if you could buy parts locally. I didn't ask Todd to come look it over. But it *was* cute. And it only cost me $900.

I borrowed one friend's truck and another friend's car trailer and hauled my new tractor to my farm. Although it didn't have a lot of power, I was happy with it. The children were ecstatic! They loved taking turns driving the tractor with Daddy. I did a little extra work on the tractor. Like installing new front and rear lights, putting on a new water pump belt, and finishing painting and reassembling the tractor. It was fun working on my first real farm tool. The tractor has come in handy. I bought a set of snow chains for it which extended its usefulness even more. I have used it to bring in full hay wagons, move and spread manure, pull my trailer all over the farm, pull logs out of the edge of the beaver pond, drag heavy dead animals, bring in firewood, and other odd jobs. Yes, I'm glad I bought it, even though I am currently somewhat looking for a larger, real tractor that I can put hay up with. And the real tractor does not have to be cute.

Back to the garden. Not only did we have to deal with the red clay soil, we also had to do something about the thistles. We have several varieties here, but the most noxious one is probably the Canadian thistle. Their roots can extend fifteen feet down into the ground with horizontal roots reaching fifteen feet out from the plant. Pollination can occur even if two plants are 300' apart! New plants can grow from severed pieces as small as 1/4" long. Studies have shown that one plant can spread more than 18 feet in a single year and the seeds can be transported to new locations on gentle two mph breezes. These are things you want to get rid of!

Two weeks after we arrived, we received a notice in the mail from the county. The notice informed us that all noxious weeds, including Canadian thistle, MUST be eradicated by June 10. Would we be put in jail for 30 days if they found a thistle on our property? Remember, we are the people who read the sign, ALL TRUCKS MUST ENTER WEIGH STATION and pulled in. To comply with the notice, we tried a number of methods of dealing with thistles. First, we bought some Roundup, a well-known and respected weed killer. The stuff cost us $6 for a small 24-ounce ready-mixed container! It should be noted that we wanted to garden organically without the use of sprays or commercial fertilizers. But we felt like we had to do something to get rid of these tough weeds.

We applied the Round-Up very selectively, just on the thistles.   Actually, Susie carefully painted each thistle individually with a sponge-type paint application, giving each one a good dousing. A few thistles did give up the ghost, temporarily, only to rebound later in the summer. It seemed to have no effect on most of the thistle plants! We increased the amount of dousing of the Roundup, but to no avail. That failing, we went to Plan B. We paid a bounty of one cent to the children for every thistle plant turned into the management. Oh, and our contract called for the removal of not just the plant, but the roots as well. So, the children grabbed their hoes and garden tools and attacked the thistles. So did Susie and I. It seemed like it would be a never ending battle - and it turned out to be just that. Control of thistles takes years of concentrated effort. They don't get tired, even though you do! My only advice is to get committed to your goal and keep at it.

As the first summer progressed, we watched as our blueberry and raspberry bushes slowly died. The grape plants also died. No need to fear. They were guaranteed by the nursery to be replaced if they died. However, the replacements also died. The prospect of eating our own berries and grapes was looking very slim.

I'll never know if the blackberry bushes would have lived and thrived. One day I was using my trusty gas-powered Weed Eater to get rid of some of the weeds in and around the garden. A Weed Eater is a handy tool designed to cut down "nasty weeds" so your plants can grow. Well, instead of just weeds, I also accidentally cut down the blackberry bushes. When Susie asked where the blackberry bushes disappeared to, my response was, "They sure must have been sickly and small for me not to notice them." I can be bad about making excuses. Which is too bad, because I'm afraid I also have a really poor record of tearing things up with my Weed Eater.

The yield of the strawberries was nonexistent that first summer. We had been told to pinch off all blossoms and just let the plants spend all their energy growing that first year. Then, we were allowed to harvest berries the second year. That was hard to do, especially since we still had to weed the little things with no apparent harvesting in sight. Patience. That is one thing that gardening calls for.

The next summer, we decided that our garden spot needed a good deep plowing and more manure worked into it. I learned of a man who does this kind of thing and gave him a call. After learning about my needs, he somewhat hesitantly said, "Well, it would take us several hours. We would need two men, two tractors and a manure spreader. I guess we would need to charge about $100. I know that's a lot of money, but that is about what we need to charge. Does that sound okay?" For someone raised in the cities and suburbs it sounded too good to be true.

On the appointed day, the men and their equipment showed up. They loaded up the first manure spreader load and started spreading it on the garden. Before the first load was even 1/4 spread, the drive chain broke on the spreader. For those who don't know what that means, it means that that spreader is not going to spread any more manure until new parts are installed. And the new parts can't be installed until the manure is out of the box. The owner started spreading the manure by hand. Meanwhile, his companion on the other tractor was trying to gather large piles of manure to spread and hit some kind of buried concrete thing. It broke off one of the teeth on his loader. So far, my little job had destroyed a spreader and a part of a loader. They were probably wondering how they were ever going to make any money working for me! As the morning wore on, many piles of manure were carried to the garden spot. Finally, a bull plow was used to plow the manure down into the "rich" red clay.

With more manure and better churned soil, we were hoping for a better garden that year. However, it was not to be. That was the wet, flood-filled summer of 1993. Everything that we had planted in the garden drowned. The only things that grew at all were a few herbs and some roses that we planted in the previous owner's garden spot (remember, it's that puny little 8 x 15 spot I made fun of earlier). Those herbs and roses grew tall, beautiful, healthy, and strong! The reason things grew there was that we removed all the building material trash, which uncovered its true state: a raised bed of pure aged manure. Now, that got us to wondering. Why keep trying to work in that big red clay garden? Why not establish our own raised bed garden and grow plants intensively (that means close to each other, so you don't have to weed so much). The only thing wrong with that plan was that we had no apparent way to move tons of aged manure to the garden spot. That is until we thought of Ed.

Ed Grube and his family own a trucking and logging company. Ed said he could move all the manure I wanted, and fast, too. He kept talking about bringing his "Michigan" to do the job. I've already confessed to you how ignorant I was of tractor makes and models and had no idea what he was referring to.

In preparation for the moving of the soil, I went to a do-it-yourself store and bought 20 old used railroad ties. These were to keep the sides of the raised bed from eroding away. We also wanted some walkways within the garden to be made out of railroad ties, so we wouldn't walk on the soil and compact it. How to bring home those greasy ties? Using the trailer, hooked up behind the van, of course. They sure were heavy.

On the agreed day, I was working in my shop, waiting for Ed to show up. Suddenly, one of those huge scoop trucks like the highway crews use pulled into the driveway. Sitting high up in the cab, with his ear protection on, was Ed. I was amazed at the size of this monster machine. I pointed out the garden spot (where I had already laid out a grid of old railroad ties) and the aged manure piles. In less than an hour he had moved enough good rich soil to create a beautiful 38' x 23' garden spot. His time cost me less than $70. What a good use of money!

The next summer, we planted in that big raised bed garden for the first time. Things went great! It was easy to pull weeds out of the loose black soil, our yields were outstanding, and gardening was suddenly fun again. We only made a few mistakes. One thing that we messed up on was the placing of certain vegetables. Everything grew much taller and more luxuriant than usual, because of the high nitrogen content in the aged manure. We planted onions "behind" the potatoes and the onions never grew well. They were shaded by the huge potato plants. Also, we didn't pinch off some of the flowers of the tomatoes like we should have, and ended up with loads of very small green tomatoes at the season's end.

Toward the end of that summer, we started thinking and planning for the next year's garden. Not surprisingly, we decided to move in more aged manure and make our garden spot even bigger. So, in the fall, we hired Ed to bring his monster machine again and move some more soil. He moved enough manure to add a 19' x 28' section to our existing garden. That created a total garden size of 1418 square feet, which is less than 1/3 the size of our garden in the red clay. However, our yields are much higher due to the better fertility of the soil and the intensive way we plant our seeds.

After we had planted our garden the next spring, a new friend, David Grapentine, came over and looked at the garden. He commented that it is not recommended to use railroad ties in the garden because the chemicals used to treat the ties cause cancer. Apparently, these chemicals can leach out into the plants. So early one morning I was in the garden, digging out all those railroad ties and dragging them away from the garden spot. It was a lot of work, but well worth it if it saves even one person from the pain and suffering of cancer. It also illustrates well another principle of life on the farm: you are never done, things are always changing. What changes will we make in our garden in future years? It will be interesting, and perhaps even backbreaking, to see.

The chapter title suggests that I am going to tell you about our orchard, so I suppose I had better start. We realized that planting an orchard is a long term process and would yield abundantly only in the long run. Thus, we felt like we needed to start the orchard our very first summer here, to at least get the clock ticking in our favor. We ordered a number of trees from reputable orchards located in our climate zone. In our first summer, we planted Courtland, Wealthy, Standard Prairie Spy and Wolf River apples. In our second summer, we added Yellow Delicious, and Red Stayman Winesap apples. We also planted Mount Royal plum trees and Kristen and Windsor cherry trees. Pear trees we planted included Beurre Bosc and Moonglow. Finally, we planted two Russian Mulberry trees to hopefully appease the birds by giving them something to eat besides our precious fruit.

To date our orchard has been anything but a rousing success. Our growing season is so short that we get very little growth in any one year. That is a nice way of saying that they are about the same size as the day we planted them. That is, except for those which have died. The field they are planted in is red clay (what did you expect?), even though we did dig a deep hole for each while planting and included some good rich aged manure. I have kept the weeds down around them so they don't have to compete for water or sunlight. During their first summer I watered them appropriately. I have wrapped them in tree wrap to prevent rodent damage that occurs in the snow months (mice burrow under the snow and eat the bark off trees). They are inspected often and pruning paint is applied to any damaged areas or where branches have broken off. I have each one in a little cage to keep deer and cows from eating their tender branches. Each has been pruned according to the instructions provided. In short, we have done all we know to do and still they are tiny little trees. We did have a few small apples on three of the trees last year and hope for more this year. My advice to new orchardists is to set your sights pretty low - at least in cold climates like we have up here.

Will we plant more trees in our orchard? It's hard to say. I think both Susie and I have a "wait and see" attitude about this part of our farm. We want to grow our own fruit, but it may be too hard given our climate and conditions. This is, however, a large apple-growing region, so it may just take longer than we had planned. We'll keep you updated!

Chapter 5
Raising Meat Chickens and Turkeys

Chickens are certainly useful for the eggs they lay. But our family also likes to eat many meals that have as their basic ingredient - chicken. Also, you've all heard the medical news stories about how chicken and turkey are low in fat and cholesterol and how we should be eating more of it and less red meat. Well, since my cholesterol was once quite high and there is a good bit of heart disease in my family, that makes the raising of chickens and turkeys even more enticing. For these reasons we decided to raise chickens and turkeys specifically for their meat.

Some things we have tried to do on the farm have ended up being a long, hard process. Not so for raising meat birds. Basically, you need a place to keep them (with lots of heat at first), water, food, and a way to kill and process them. All parts of this process are not equally fun, but the end result sure is delicious.

If you are someone who does not want to read about butchering animals, please don't worry. You can read on ahead and I'll warn you when I am about to talk about killing and you can skip that section. Promise!

First, you need to place an order for the birds. As with laying hens, there are many types to choose from. Our hatchery offers the following: Super Jumbo Cornish Cross, Rock-Cornish Game, Indian River Broiler Cross, and Premium Broilers. You can also use some of the smaller meat-type chicks (that are also laying birds) like Rhode Island Reds, Hisex Browns, Arbor Acre Browns, Barred Rock, Black Austalorps, White Rocks, and Black Sex Links. We asked Phyllis at the feed store and she suggested the Super Jumbo Cornish Cross. They grow very quickly and have few problems. About the biggest problem is that their legs don't grow as fast as they should and you can have a good number of lame chickens. The other problem is that they, like many Americans, don't always know when to stop eating. If you don't restrict their food, starting about the fourth week, some will end their lives the victim of a heart attack. Yes, they just stiffen up and die right on the spot! It's pretty sobering when you realize that you could be doing the same thing to your own body. We buy straight-run, which means that we accept both males and females. If you specify just cockerels (those are the males), you end up paying a little more per bird. Cocks grow faster and bigger than hens (the females).

For turkeys, our choices are fewer: Broadbreasted White, Bronze, Bourbon Red, and Royal Palm. The first year, we chose the old-fashioned Bronze, which looks a lot like the wild turkeys you have seen in books. They worked out well for us, although they are a little slower growing. This year we chose the Broadbreasted White, a little bit faster growing bird that can have leg problems. When you buy a turkey in the grocery store, chances are good that it is a Broadbreasted White.

You need a place to keep the meat birds. We start ours out in the chick house that I described earlier when talking about our laying hens. In fact, we usually start the laying hens and meat birds together. It saves on energy costs and cuts down on chore time (if you are going to feed and water one kind of bird, it is just as easy to put a little more out for the other kind of bird). Starting the meat birds in the chick house has always worked well for us. Well, almost always.

We use fresh wood chips for bedding and keep adding another layer every few days. I buy the chips from a local sawmill for around $5 a pickup-sized load (and they load it for me, too!). You don't want to use sawdust because it can get in the birds' lungs and mess them up pretty badly. You also don't want to use straw or hay because it can be dusty or moldy and give the little chicks lung diseases. Besides, it would be very easy to catch straw or hay on fire with your heat lamp being placed so low to the floor. I've never had a strong desire to wake up in the middle of the night to the smell of burning chicks.

When we bring the chicks home, we have the bed of wood chips all ready for them. We also have two or three little quart waterers that we dip each chick's beak into as we unload them (just to be sure they know what that red waterer is for!). This dipping is a job that the children enjoy doing. Seems like just about anyone has the ability to handle dipping a bird's beak in water. Of course, there must be a best way to do it, else I wouldn't often hear one child say to another one, "No, not like that. Look, you do it like this . . . "

We have chick food on paper plates for them to eat and a few start walking around and eating some right away. Unlike the smart and cute little laying hens that scratch around for their food, these meat birds just drop their beaks and eat. Instead of using the usual medicated chick starter, we have always chosen to use unmedicated chick food (called "game bird starter") because we don't want our food to be all drugged up when we eat it.

It is also important to have new chicks in a place with no corners. If there are corners, they might huddle together and smother the ones in the very corner. You must keep in mind that chicks are not the smartest things in the world. Reminds me of football and soccer games I have heard about, where people were crushed and smothered when they got trapped in a swelling, wild crowd--are we as smart as we think we are? Our solution to the chick crowding is a low-tech one. We just tack a piece of cardboard up for a temporary wall and make sure it is rounded at all "corners." [I offer this bit of information free of charge. Operators of football stadiums take note. If you can find a way to use rounded cardboard to save a life, great!]

I have read many books about starting chicks and most have very precise instructions. Seems you are supposed to have the temperature at an exact level each week of their life. The hatchery that sells us our chicks gives the following temperature schedule (at chick height): first week at 90-92° F, second week at 88-90° F, third at 85-88° F, fourth at 80-85° F, fifth at 75-80° F, sixth at 70-75° F. I have never been able to achieve the temperatures suggested for those first couple of weeks. It is just too cold up here for me to heat the chick house up to those levels in April or May, or even June. But, we have had wonderful success every time. Well, almost every time. The only thermostat I use is myself. I walk out to the chick house. If they seem too hot or cold, I adjust the lights. Not real complicated or high-tech, but it works.

I must admit that I look out of my bedroom window during the night to make sure that I can still see the lights are working. I would hate to wake up some morning and find that the power went out in the chick house during the night. I also open my bedroom window and listen to see if the chicks are sending out S.O.S. signals (you learn to tell the difference between a distress chirp and a contented chirp). And yes, I have left the warm comfort of my bedroom in the night and gone out to check on my chicks. I rarely ask Susie to go out and check for me, but I do usually wake her up (if she is asleep) and tell her that I am going out. I'm sure she wants to know.

After the first week it's important to ventilate the chick house. All of the moisture from 125 birds needs to go somewhere. Chicks need fresh air, but can't handle drafts. Solution? Open the window or windows for brief periods of time. I don't use any scientific humidity-checking tools, I just walk out and check out the amount of moisture on the inside of the windows. If it looks like a lot, I open up. That solution has always worked for me. Well, almost always.

After anywhere from two to four weeks, we move our chicks into the barn. By now, they have started losing their pretty yellow feathers, and are replacing them with white ones-this is called molting. Some are quite ugly creatures about this time, with practically no feathers at all because they are in the middle of their molt. Their transportation to the barn is via a cardboard box carefully relayed by none other than the firm of CCCTMI (Castleberry Children Chicken and Turkey Movers, Incorporated).

In the barn they are placed in a coop I have made just for the meat birds. The first summer I built a 13 feet by 12 ½ feet coop using chicken wire. The wire extends all the way from the floor to the ceiling in an effort to keep predators out. The next year I enlarged it to 26 feet x 12 ½ feet, plenty of room for 125 meat birds. The birds have their own door and a yard which they can use to catch a few rays of sun. The turkeys love the yard, but the meat chickens don't really seem to want to go outside--they just want to pretty much hang their stomachs over the side of the feeder and eat! But that's okay because things have always worked out well for us. Well, almost always.

I keep noting that things almost always work for me, and they really have. I have very successfully started six batches of birds in the chick house in the last three years, and my losses have been much lower than those expected by the hatchery. You are going to lose some birds. It's just a fact of life. But things didn't go so well in our first batch.

You see, we got our first batch of 135 meat birds last year on the very first possible date - April 13. That may not seem very early to my friends in Florida, but I don't live in Florida! We put them in the chick house, just like always. We used lots of fresh wood chips, just like always. We gave them fresh water and food, just like always. Then they started dying. And dying. And dying. We talked to the feed store and the hatchery. We thought that maybe the chicks had contracted a lung infection or pneumonia and the chickens were passing it around. We decided to give them a high dose of vitamins, something we had never done before. At least the vitamins weren't medicine. Still, they died. I cleaned out their chick house completely and started over with fresh bedding. I also moved some to the barn to avoid crowding and hopefully break this cycle. Still, they died. Finally, when they were about four weeks old I set a decision rule: If any four died in one day, or if fifteen total more died then I would wipe out the whole group and start over again. It didn't sound like fun to me and I sure didn't want to go to that extreme. I didn't want us to get any disease by eating diseased meat either! But then the Lord blessed us and they stopped dying. They started looking and acting healthy again. The last weeks saw only a very few deaths. Only 89 of the original 135 birds made it to the end.

What caused the deaths? It is possible that we just got a bad batch from the hatchery, a rare but possible situation. They claimed that no one else was having problems like we were, and I believe them. It is also possible that rats were somehow infecting them. We had never had problems with rats before (in fact, had never seen a rat in the barn before), but had a really big problem with them during the time in question. It is also possible that the weather was just too cold for them. We were unable to get the temperature above 50 degrees in the chick house for several days during their first week of life. We also had a snow storm during their early weeks, with near blizzard conditions at times. As a result, I was unable to open the windows and let the trapped humidity out of the chick house for fear that the chicks would freeze. Whatever the reason is that so many died, I am happy to say that our second batch that year went very smoothly. What lesson did we learn? Probably, not to get our chicks so early again.

Don't think that we just put these meat birds in a cage and walk away for eight weeks. There are so many things that we have learned by carefully watching their behavior. For example, there comes a time at around four weeks of age that the roosters' male hormones seem to "kick in." If there is one thing a mature rooster can't stand, it is to have another rooster around. Well, in our coop each rooster has to live with about 60 other roosters and so it gets pretty interesting when they start trying to establish control of the group. Two roosters will run up to each other, lift themselves high on their feet, stare each other down for about two seconds, and then . . . well, then they just sit down. Thought I was going to tell you how they battle it out to the death, with scenes of flying feathers and bloody heads, didn't you? But remember, these are fat, lazy meat birds that pretty much just want to eat. About the only time blows are exchanged is when a rooster comes upon a sick or crippled bird. Then it will peck the poor bird's head unmercifully. It is really sad to watch. My solution is to separate the crippled birds from the well ones. Of course, then some of the crippled ones who are a little bit stronger than the other crippled ones will sometimes bully the ones who are worse off. That is the way life is. You can't pretend that it's not.

Turkey toms (those are the males) will also fight. Two toms will strut toward each other with their feathers puffed out fully. They will then grab each other's wattles (that is the thing hanging down under their beak) and the thing that hangs off the top of their beak (I don't know what that is called) and push each other around. The battle ends when one spots food or they both fall in the ditch.

Toms will also attack you, especially if you are wearing something bright blue and red. You see, when they strut around and fight, their head turns bright blue and their neck turns red. If you are wearing those colors, they think you must be openly demonstrating superiority and thus they feel they have to attack you. Note: This is just what we think they are thinking. In reality, no turkey has ever gone on the record, either in writing or verbally, to clearly spell out what they are thinking. They usually won't attack you head on, but will bop you in the back when you are turned away from them. And it really hurts--those beaks are tough and sharp! Just ask Jeannie, whose back hurt for several weeks after getting bopped by Biggie.

Yes, we name our turkeys because they usually have very distinct personalities. In addition to Biggie, we've raised Socrates, Plato, Aristotle, Alexander the Great, Yorker, Cyrus-King-of- Persia, and Tommy. Most names came from whatever history the children were studying in homeschool.

Sometimes, rather than our chickens and turkeys going after each other, things will go after our chickens and turkeys. As mentioned before, we have lots of wild creatures in our area and many of them just love to eat fresh meat birds! We've had a number of hawks in our barn and have seen an eagle flying high overhead. But the biggest headache for us are raccoons. If we still have birds left in early autumn, they will find a way to get in and have a feast. They are smart enough to open a latched door. They will even tear apart your screen or fence if it is not stapled down securely. They must go over the whole fence until they find your one weak spot. A naturalist will say they are having a feeding frenzy in preparation for the upcoming winter months. I have no problem with that, as long as they leave my animals alone. I have tried just about everything to catch racoons in our barn but with very little success. Those boogers are smart as all get out (another thing people say where I come from). I bought a live trap (which means it won't kill your animal, it will just trap it so you can release it somewhere it might be more wanted) and baited it with sardines. A friend of mine had told me, "They just can't resist sardines." My racoons weren't interested in sardines, but one of the cats was, so I caught it instead. Then someone said, "Use marshmallows for bait. They just love marshmallows!" I guess my racoons must have been raised near a health food store or by a registered dietician, because they didn't want any marshmallows either.

One day I set my live trap and went for a walk with Susie. As we returned, I noticed that the trap had closed. I had a coon! I looked through the door casually and saw something furry that was too big to be a cat in the trap. I was elated! I had finally captured one of those smart creatures that was causing me so much trouble. When I returned to the barn with my gun, I looked carefully in the cage. Inside was a large black and white skunk. What a mess! Now what was I supposed to do? If I picked up the cage to carry it outside it would probably spray me (not a good plan). If I tried to open the cage and let it go free it would probably spray me (again, not a good plan). So, not knowing anything else to do, I took a shot at it with my rifle from about 20 feet away, hoping that it couldn't spray that far away. Well, it just lay down and started dying, and as it did, a sound filled the air - somewhat like air coming out of a tire. I wondered if I had shot another tire, but no, I was in a barn and no tires were around. Then my nostrils gave my brain a little hint of what the sound was. The skunk was dying, to be sure. But he was also leaving behind a "tangible" symbol of his being there. He was spraying the barn with his awful spray. After he stopped moving, and the air-coming-out-of-the-tire sound stopped, I ran over and carried the trap out of the barn. Needless to say, my clothes and hair smelled very bad when I went into the house. I have learned that tomato juice is a natural antidote for skunk spray and have several cans standing by for future emergencies. The smell in the barn lasted many months. Before winter arrived that year, I ended up having to kill several skunks in my live trap.

Okay, time to get serious. I bought several snap traps (these traps will injure or kill the animal that puts its foot in) and baited above the trap with some chicken parts. I sat in my house rocking in my chair, listening for them. I would hear some rattling and run out to the barn with a rifle in my hand, only to find that something else had made the noise or that the racoon was nowhere in sight. One night I put some food in a garbage can outside my bedroom window. Right after doing this I looked out and saw a coon near the can, so I knew the coons were out. As soon as I would hear the can being pushed over, I would run down with my gun, but never got a shot at a coon. Finally, I decided to do what they do in western novels-set up a trap and just "wait it out." I set up the "food-in-the-garbage-can" trap and stood behind a tree 30 feet away with my gun loaded. I was determined to stand there until morning if need be in order to get my coon. But my determination didn't last. After about 40 minutes, I gave up and came inside, believing that nothing was going to come around again that night. In a few minutes, I heard the garbage can being turned over and the feeding frenzy beginning. Disgusted, I just closed my window and turned on the fan so I wouldn't have to listen to it. I'm almost sure I heard that racoon giggle. Once again, I was not successful in "bringing home the coon."

Butchering

Well, most of the chickens and turkeys do survive all of the assaults of predators and disease. Which means we need to butcher and process them. I am going to talk about that now, so if you don't want to read it, please skip to the next chapter.

We butcher our meat chickens at eight weeks of age. At first we kept them until ten weeks, but decided that the extra weight we achieved wasn't worth the extra chicken feed we had to put into them. Besides, by killing them at eight weeks, we cut off two weeks opportunity from the racoons! We do wait longer for the turkeys until we feel they are as big as we want them, which is usually around fifteen weeks. If it is getting late in the fall, though, and the racoons start killing the turkeys (and they usually kill the biggest and best turkey first!), I go ahead and butcher the rest of them right away.

The first step is to take away their food the afternoon before you will butcher. This helps to make the whole process cleaner because they won't have food in their gizzards. Make sure you let them have water, however. On the morning of the butchering, we get everything ready. This includes putting up a clothesline with small pieces of string hanging down about every two feet. We also get together knives, tables, clean water, buckets, several large clean empty waste cans, and cutting boards. The chickens are caught and carried, hanging upside down by their feet, to the clothesline. Believe it or not, this helps to calm them down. Then they are hung, upside down by their feet on the strings. Most quickly calm down and just look at the world with a new upside-down perspective. The butcher (Daddy) then inserts a knife through the mouth up into the head, and twists the knife, "killing" the brain so the chicken can't feel any pain. The knife is next inserted down the throat and a slit made on the main artery. The chicken then bleeds to death. We prefer this method to cutting their heads off, because we avoid having headless chickens running around the barnyard getting their muscles tensed (which could result in tough meat). It also seems more humane, since they feel no pain. Another advantage is cleaner meat, since most of the blood has drained out. After the chickens have bled and died, they are taken down and brought to the butchering table. First, the head and feet are removed. We don't eat either, although chicken feet are becoming a new delicacy. Then the chickens are plucked.

You remove feathers by dipping the bird in very hot water for about five seconds, and then plucking the feathers. The hot water loosens the feathers. Plucking is not a fun job. It is very hard to get all of the tiny pinfeathers off. Also, the feathers tend to, well, stink after they are dipped in the hot water. There is a chicken plucker that you can use to speed up the process. We can rent one from our feed store for $5 a day, not a bad investment. More recently, we have started skinning our birds, bypassing the need to pluck at all. To skin you just make a slit in the skin up the chicken's middle and pull the skin off. The only downside is that skinless birds tend to dry out if you are baking them (which isn't a problem for us since we bake very few hens).

After plucking (or de-skinning) you next open up the body cavity and remove all the guts and stuff inside. The first time we butchered, Uncle Jim came to help us and brought along his children. He is the one who, more than anyone else, taught us how to raise and butcher chickens and turkeys. At one time in his life he had worked in the butcher section of a grocery store.

Anyway, as we were pulling the stuff out of the inside of the chickens (this is called de-gutting), Jim told us to put some of the guts into one bucket and everything else into another bucket. I asked him why we needed to separate what looked to me like garbage. "Oh," he said, "we take the stuff in this bucket home. We clean it up good, and then cook it on low for about three hours . . . " At this point, my eyes must have been getting bigger and bigger. I was actually getting nauseated and could easily picture him cooking this garbage and then eating it. Yuck! I made a quick mental note to decline any future offers for meals at his house. After a few minutes of struggling with a chicken he continued, " . . . and then after it has cooked for a couple of hours we feed it to our dogs." Boy, talk about being relieved! We have eaten at Jim's house several times and have found the food to be great. I guess my worry was due to things we have seen other people actually eat. I knew a girl from Thailand and she invited Susie and me to her apartment once for a traditional Thai dinner. In one of the pots were several sheep's eyeballs floating around and kind of looking at me. That's one thing we didn't care to try.

After de-gutting, you rinse the chicken well, and toss it into one of the clean large garbage cans that is filled with ice cold water. You process all of the chickens in the same way until all of your meat is in those cans. Then, it's usually time to grab a bite of lunch (which rarely consists of chicken in any form) before going further.

After lunch, we pull the cooled chicken out of the can and cut it into pieces. This is a really easy job if you know what you are doing. First you cut off the legs. Then you cut off the wings. Finally you make two cuts down the backbone and remove the back. All you are left with is the breast, which is split into two pieces. You are now through cutting up the chicken, so you rinse it well and wrap it in freezer paper. Place the wrapped meat in a plastic ziplock bag and you're done. We can butcher and process 125 chickens in about eight hours. But it's a hard eight hours!

The first year, we only had one upright freezer which was not large enough to hold all of our meat, fruits, and vegetables. So we rented freezer locker space at a nearby grocery store. At $6 a month, it seemed like a cheap alternative to buying another freezer. It was also nice that the meat froze very quickly in the grocer's freezer, as compared to how fast it would freeze in our home freezer. The disadvantage was having to go to the grocery store every now and then to bring home our meat and thus replenish our home supply. Later, we bought another upright freezer, a good decision in our estimation.

Butchering turkeys is about the same as meat chickens. Sometimes they are really big and require more effort to kill. Last year, I had to shoot them with my .22-caliber rifle because they were too large. No one would hold them while I whacked off their heads, and I couldn't get my knife down their throats far enough to slit the artery. The biggest difference is that we always pluck them now because they will all be baked. We tried just skinning them one year, but were very dissatisfied with the cooked result. The outside meat was tough and chewy, just as you would expect.

The one thing that I can't adequately relate in this written form is the taste of home raised meat birds. It is delicious! The meat has flavor and is so tender. When we once ran out of meat and had to buy some at the store, it was incredible how poorly the store meat tasted. Another thing that has amazed us is the size of our cuts. Our chicken breasts are about twice the size of the largest ones you can buy in the store.

Earlier I related how I am supposed to be careful about what I eat and how I try to cut down on fats and cholesterol. As a result, I have had an agreement with my neighbor, Jeff, about the meat chickens I raise. After we butcher, he gets all the dark meat and I get all the breast meat. For this he shares in the cost of feeding the chicken and helps butcher if he is available. He feels like he is a winner and so do we!

So what does this meat cost us? I keep good records and the final cost per bird (including feed, grit, and wood chips but not including electricity) has ranged from $3.13 to $5.00. Considering that a dressed bird weighs out at around 5 ½ pounds that means our meat cost us between 57¢- 91¢ per pound. Even if it cost us five times that much we would still choose to raise our own meat birds. The flavor, the fact that they have not been medicated, and the extra care we take in butchering and processing would be well worth any costs we might incur in feed.

Besides, if we didn't raise our own meat birds, we might miss out on all the fun of racoons!

Chapter 6
Horse Fever!

What girl doesn't dream of riding and owning a horse? Well, my daughter Jeannie is no exception. Ever since she was eight years old, she has been reading about, looking at, asking about, and dreaming about owning her own horse. It seemed like a perfectly safe and honorable goal so we encouraged her. We would check out books from the library about horses, drive slowly anytime we passed horses in a field, took every opportunity we had to get close to horses, and rode horses at riding stables when we were near them. We found coloring books that had horses as their main topic and wall posters of horses. In sum, we fed her horse fever.

After moving to the farm we were very busy the first year just getting everything in liveable condition. But as our second summer rolled around, we started talking about making Jeannie's dream a reality. She had always been such a good girl, never begging to get a horse, and we wanted her to have one. She was 11 years old at the time, and we knew of girls her age who already had horses and seemed to be doing pretty well with them. It was time.

I've bought ten cars, two motorcycles, and several boats in my life. I have also bought three homes and all the things that go in them. As a marketing professor, I have researched and taught students the fundamentals of how consumers go about buying things. With all that experience and knowledge I feel like I have a pretty good idea of how to make a wise purchase. It's simple. You gather information, find out who has what you want, and make your decision. You then bring it home and you're set. Right? Not for horses! Let me try to explain.

As you read the list of things I have bought, you will recognize that all of those things are missing one thing that horses have: a personality. Although there are certainly some differences, basically a 1985 Plymouth Voyager with 100,000 miles is like all of the other 1985 Plymouth Voyagers with 100,000 miles. And when you call the owner, you can ask all kinds of meaningful questions like: How are the tires? Do the brakes work well? What kind of gas mileage does it get? Is it rusted at all? When did it last have a tuneup? Is there anything mechanical that is starting to wear out to your knowledge? Then you can pretty much make up your mind, based on that phone call, whether to go and see the car or not.

Not so for horses. One quarter horse born three years ago is *not* pretty much like another quarter horse born three years ago. One horse can be easy to groom, while the second one won't even let you lift his feet to check them. One horse will run at the least little thing, while you can't get the second to trot for all your life. One horse has been trained to ride Western-style while the second has been trained to ride English-style. One horse doesn't mind being alone, while the second just has to have other horses around. One horse wants to be ridden while the second wants to eat your expensive grain and take a nap instead. You get the picture? The result is that it's not as easy as buying a car. You can't just call someone up on the phone and gather a bunch of hard, cold facts about a horse. To have any feel at all about a horse you really have to go and look at him or her.

But what to look for? I am probably like a lot of people. I look for a pretty horse that doesn't seem too wild. But looks are not all that important, it's the personality that you should be concerned about. As a total novice, though, I had no idea how to assess a horse's personality just by looking at it. However, we were blessed to know friends in the area who were willing and ready to help us out.

One day Uncle Jim came to pick up one of the steers he was keeping on my farm. Paul Stein, the man who drove the trailer for Jim, said he raised Morgan horses just a few miles from our farm. And yes, we were welcome to come out and take a look at them anytime. Talking to Jeannie, I learned that Morgans are supposed to be some kind of a wonder horse. They are gentle, strong, have good dispositions, and are raised for pleasure riding, buggy driving, or for use as a work horse. Sounded good to me, so we drove over and took a look at them.

The Morgans were beautiful animals! There was one that we fell in love with, Belle, but she was not for sale. Isn't that always the way it seems to go? I couldn't blame Naomi Stein for wanting to keep her. Belle was a very gentle and beautiful horse. Well, we visited their farm several more times and they finally decided to sell Belle, if we would agree to several conditions. What they really wanted was another "baby" from Belle. Would we agree to buy Belle but let them breed her back and keep the foal? They would pay all expenses. All we had to do was let her return to their farm right about the time the foal was to be born. Sounded great to us! As this deal was unfolding, they located another Morgan that they thought would work for us by the name of Lady Beth. So, since horses like company, and Stevie also wanted to have a horse, we decided to buy both horses.

But we didn't bring them home right away. The Steins were kind enough to give us lessons on how to groom, ride, and take care of horses. We made many visits to their farm learning these lessons. It was during these trips that we changed our minds about Lady Beth. She seemed too high strung for our inexperienced riders. That was no problem. The Steins are wonderful people. They want you to be totally satisfied with anything you purchase from them and back this with a complete money-back guarantee. Belle seemed great and she gave wonderful rides for all the children when we visited the Steins' farm. Finally, the day came when she was delivered to our farm. Again, the Steins went well beyond the call of duty. They not only delivered her, they also kept checking on us to see that everything was going okay in those first critical days.

I need to back up a second. I said they brought her to our home, but before you bring a horse home you have to get everything ready. Now I've brought seven beautiful babies home from the hospital and I know something about getting everything ready for them. I know how to set up cribs, get the cradle in place, and look for those ever-disappearing child-proof plug protectors. But it's not that easy for a horse.

First, we had to check the pasture over to make sure there wasn't something out there that a horse could trip over or step into. We found plenty! There was an old axle and wheel in the bottom of the hollow that would be perfect for horses to kill themselves on. So, along with the help of about six boys, I pushed and coaxed that thing to the top of the steep hill. Then I noticed that some previous owner had dragged the ditch cleaner out from the barn and left it in the pasture to rust. This tool, as it winds its way around inside the barn, cleans the manure out that is located in the ditch. The farmer simply parks his manure spreader underneath the chute at the end of the barn, and all of the manure slides right in. It really works well. But ours was out in the pasture. I asked Todd to come over and drag it out with his big tractor, which he most graciously did. Later he cut it up with his blow torch for the scrap iron.

Now was the pasture ready? Hardly. Our pasture has a deep gully running its entire length. Someone had placed two large metal culverts together to make a bridge for cattle to cross from one side to the other. However, the two culverts didn't meet in the middle, and the eight-inch space was a perfect place for a horse to break its leg. Well, just move the culverts together, you might say. I don't think I could have, even with dynamite, because they were so buried in the red clay mud. Instead, I placed a railroad tie in the crack. The tie was long enough so that it rested on each side of the hill, thus closing up my gap. The pasture was also the home to lots of big, jagged rocks and old boards and these had to be removed.

I next had to make a stable in the barn for those times when the weather was too rainy or the horses were ready to give birth. Wood is a good choice, except that horses like to chew on wood. If you use pressure treated wood, they won't chew on it as much, but do you want your horse eating even a little of the cancer-causing treated wood? We decided to set up a temporary stable just using several long metal gates. These gates had five bars running horizontally and seemed sturdy enough to keep a horse from escaping.

The barn had another hazard for horses. You know those

manure ditches I talked about? Well, even though the mechanical ditch cleaner had been removed, the ditches themselves were still there. They are about 10" deep and 12" wide. I could have poured concrete and filled them in, but with about 240 feet of ditch, that would get quite expensive. Being a frugal man, I decided to just cover the ditches with boards. To do this I bought 3/4" plywood and 10" pressure treated wood. I cut the plywood into 2' x 8' pieces and nailed each piece, at a 90 degree angle, to one eight-foot piece of pressure treated wood. This created a wooden "bridge" shaped like an "L" that I would place down in the ditch. This solution has worked well, and was quite inexpensive.

Okay, enough preparation? Hardly. How about buying all the stuff you need to take care of a horse? I was amazed at the amount of stuff we needed to buy. A partial list would include the following: Cotton lead ropes $3.35, leather curb chain $2.95, Kopertox medicine $5.45, Repel-X P insect repellent $15.95, Zimecterin wormer paste (every eight weeks) $9.49, loose jaw colt bit $29.87, halters $7.50, headstall $16.95, split reins $9.35, Ultra Shield spray $11.25, a 15" western saddle $190, a Mexican pony saddle $135, a youth saddle $150, liniment $15.55, hoof picks (better buy them by the dozen because you will lose about a dozen a week!) 69¢ each, hoof rasp $15.95, cutting nippers $44.95, rubber curry combs $1.65, mane and tail comb 95¢, grooming brushes $4.45, leather punch $5.55, hackamore bit $18.95, riding helmet $39.95, girths $6.95, saddle blankets $17.25, etc. . . .   Again, thankfully, we had the help of several friends who helped us understand what we needed to buy and what we could do without. They also bought this stuff for us at a discount when they would go to a Farm and Fleet store.

Back to the first few days with our new horse. As I mentioned, the Steins kept checking on us to make sure everything was going okay. Belle settled down and seemed to be doing fine. She was missing her foal (which was already over a year old, but still liked to nurse sometimes) but she took to us pretty well. She would let the children ride her. Even the little children could ride her bareback. She was one of those horses that you can just walk up to in a pasture and climb on for a ride.

As days went by however, Belle got more lonely for other horses. Horses need other horses. She started spending most of her time at the southwest corner of our pasture, looking longingly at the Bitner's cows half a mile away. We weren't sure if she thought they might be horses. Anyway, she started getting moody and less enthralled with us. It got so bad that we couldn't even ride her. The problem was probably with us. We were new to this and still didn't know everything about how to take care of a horse. Finally, Belle began to try to throw Jeannie off every time she tried to ride, and even tried to bite Jeannie. That just wasn't like Belle and we made the tough decision, after having her only two weeks, to let her return to the Steins. I am convinced that we did the best thing. We would have probably just ended up taking a good horse, and ruining her.

Where to turn to now? We started making phone calls and looking at horses. I wish I had kept track of the amount of time we spent trying to track down a good, gentle family horse! One guy even brought a few horses to our farm for us to try out. We finally enlisted the help of our friend, Ann Glavan. Ann knows horses! She trains them, gives riding lessons, has a bunch of horses herself, and just basically knows all about horses. Best of all, she likes to shop for horses, even for other people. Ann made tons of phone calls (knowing the kinds of questions to ask) and set up for us to go and look at a few. She always went with us and gave us her expert opinion. She would ride the horses and see how they would act in various situations.

It was Ann that put us in touch with Karen. Karen was moving to Texas and wouldn't be able to take all of her horses with her. She had a registered Arabian mare and a registered Pinto for sale. Ann, Susie, and the children went out to look them over. Arabs aren't known as being particularly gentle horses. Yet these horses acted fine. Everyone was impressed with them. The Pinto was one of the most beautiful horses I have ever seen.

I've learned in life that things are not always what they appear to be. When we lived in Georgia there was a beautiful old house on the grounds of the state forestry research station. It had a neat wide front porch and an old-fashioned swing. One day, I took my family for an outing to that house. We couldn't get in (the doors were locked), but we were able to take a bunch of pictures, look in the windows, walk on the paths, swing on the swing, and play in the shade of the big front porch. We stayed there quite a while and had a lot of fun. A few weeks later, I was talking to a student in the forestry program about the neat old house. "Yeah, that's where the department head gets to live. It's pretty neat all right!" he said. "What? You mean someone is living there *now*?" I asked. "Sure," he said. And we thought it was a house that had been converted to a forestry office of some kind! Boy, did we feel like a bunch of hicks! Things are not always what they seem.

Karen was willing to sell the horses to us. She wanted them to go to a home where they would be loved and well cared for. Fine. She did make one stipulation, however. "I won't sell them to you unless your pasture consists of board fencing or electric fencing." She didn't want the horses to get spooked and jump through barbed wire fence. I can understand that. It is not a pretty sight. Karen told us that when Savannah was a foal, some bigger horses had chased her through a barbed wire fence and she had been hurt very badly.

I didn't want to put up an electric fence. We were trying to reduce our use of electricity and I didn't want the children to be accidentally shocked. But after thinking it over for a while, I decided to put up the electric fence. Let's see, that added about another $175 to the cost of "horse fever." I must state that I am glad I put up the electric fence though, because it has come in handy in adding temporary pasture for the other animals and making sure they stay where I put them.

Finally, the day arrived that would see us pick up our two horses, Savannah (the Arab) and Nanibijou (the Pinto). Karen was obviously very attached to her horses and hated to see them go. We were blessed in the ease with which they loaded in the Glavans' stock trailer (thanks, Fred and Ann, for taking time to go and help us pick up our horses!) with amazing ease. We drove them home and let them loose in the pasture. It had been one month and one day since Belle had left the farm so it was nice to see horses running in the field again. And boy, did they run! They ran all over the pasture, checking it out and chasing the cows around. I just knew one of them would break a leg or something.

After a day or so, they settled down pretty well, and we were able to start riding them. A horse is not like a car or truck. You want to drive a car? Just jump in, turn the key, and you're off. When you're through driving a car, you cut off the switch and step out. Not so with a horse. First, you have to get all of your tack together (including saddle, blanket, bridle, and riding helmet). Don't forget your hoof pick, curry comb, stiff brush, soft brush, scraper, and fly spray. Then you have to catch the horse and put a halter on him to bring him back to the barn where you tie his halter to a post. After checking him all over to make sure he has no cuts or scrapes, you have to clean the hooves with your hoof pick. This requires the horse to cooperate because it is almost impossible to pick up a horse's leg if he refuses! Then you need to do all of the brushing and scraping to make sure the hair is laying flat. If it is fly season, you probably have already sprayed him down with insect repellent just so he will stand still. Then it is time to put on the blanket and saddle and tighten the girth. Finally, you have to replace the halter with the bridle. This can be touchy because there is a period of time there where nothing is holding the horse from running away. Also, it can be hard to get the horse to "take the bit" into his mouth. When all of this has been successfully done, you put on your safety helmet, check the girth to make sure it is still tight, and go for your ride. When you return, you have to do pretty much everything I have mentioned in reverse. It takes a lot of time. A lot more time than I thought it would.

Savannah, the Arab, was sort of supposed to be Jeannie's horse and Nanibijou (also called Bijou) was sort of Stevie's horse. As the children started riding the horses, we started noticing little "traits." You know, like Bijou just didn't want to do anything when Stevie was on his back. Stevie would tell the horse to get moving and Bijou would just sit there. So Stevie would kick his sides and do everything he knew to do. Still Bijou just stood there. I think he knew he was beautiful, and his pride gave the dark side to his personality. Anyway, it was no fun, and riding horses was supposed to be fun. Also Bijou and Savannah didn't really care for all the grooming and preparation work that was necessary before each ride. They would buck around and basically make a nuisance of themselves. Was this the thrill we were supposed to have from owning our own horses?

Jeannie kept her chin up. She was a very determined little girl and wasn't going to let a little 1000 pound horse push her around. Still, with her 90 pounds of determination, she wasn't much of a match at times for Savannah. So I was called in to help out. Now you have to keep in mind that I didn't have this same love affair for horses. In fact, I didn't have a horse coloring book or wall posters or anything. I still tried to help Jeannie clean Savannah's hooves and get Savannah to take the bit. I'm afraid I failed more times than I succeeded.

When we got pretty frustrated, we called in the big guns: Ann Glavan. She came right over and worked with Savannah. It was amazing to see how she controlled that horse. She could get Savannah to do just about anything she wanted. Could the problem be us? Perhaps, at least to some degree. Jeannie and Stevie continued taking lessons on their new horses to learn how to control them better.

During this time, the horses were establishing a sort of pecking order. Bijou decided that he was going to be the "top banana," Savannah would be his "slave," and the cows were held in contempt by both horses. It was amazing to watch Bijou boss Savannah around. In fact, we started seeing Bijou as a schoolyard bully, teaching bad tricks to Savannah. When we tried to separate the two, as some suggested, Savannah would totally blow up. She would start to run around like she had lost her mind. Not a good kind of horse to ride. Bijou even tried to boss around the children. Once, he pushed Jeannie into the electric fence. Not a good kind of horse to have.

Although it was only August, I knew that winter would be

here soon. I started worrying about what to do with the horses during snow storms and bad rain storms. I didn't want to keep them in the barn because animals just don't do well if they are stuck inside a barn with the potential of moldy hay around. Several people suggested that I build a loafing shed for them. I looked at a few and decided to just use an existing lean-to off the barn. This shed, which was used to keep farm equipment out of the weather, was certainly large enough and tall enough (it slopes from about 8 feet high to about 20 feet high).   It is protected on the west side by the barn. I decided to enclose half of the shed as a loafing area for the animals. To do this, I used scrap wood and built walls about eight feet high along the north side. Thus, I ended up with a two sided shed with a good solid roof. Since most storms come out of the northwest, the animals could enter the shed and keep dry and warm.

I also had to reroof the shed and used roll roofing for that job. The roll roofing goes on fast and easy, but does not last as long as a cut-shingle roof. As I was working in this shed, I came across a big plant that needed to be cut out of the way. Using my hands, I started pulling the plant. Suddenly my hands started stinging like crazy. It felt like I had a million little splinters in my hands. I had just been introduced to stinging nettle, something you want to stay away from!

Savannah continued to be a real "pill." I didn't know how we were going to solve this problem. Then one morning, less than four weeks after we got Savannah, I walked outside and happened to look over near the barn. "That looks like Savannah is outside the fence," I thought. Sure enough she was! And she was bleeding all over her legs and back. Apparently she had jumped through the barbed wire *and* electric fence. It was a bad enough cut to call in the vet.

After applying 20 stitches (which are actually staples nowadays) the vet handed me a vial and some needles. "You'll need to give her a shot of this every day. Be careful how you do it. Push the needle into the muscle tissue and then pull the plunger back a little bit just to make sure you haven't hit a blood vessel instead. If you give her these shots directly in her blood vessels it will kill her. Okay, after you see that you are not in a blood vessel, just push the plunger in and the medicine will be injected automatically. Give her these shots for the next 10 days, then I will come back out and remove the staples. Here's some stuff to spray on her wound. And we need to keep her from removing the staples."

Sure. Now I'm supposed to play vet to this crazy horse!? Actually, it wasn't that hard to give her the shots once we caught her and held her still. Because the flies were so bad, Savannah kept twitching her muscles. This resulted in her losing all of her staples. That made the wound really bad and it started looking infected. Another vet came out and gave us some cream to put on the wound. Within two weeks it had healed up about as good as it was going to. Jeannie tried riding Savannah, but things continued to go poorly.

Our decision was to sell her. But who is going to buy a horse that has jumped though a fence and had stitches just a month and a half ago? We called Ann Glavan and she told of us a family that might be interested, especially if we threw in 100 bales of hay to help get the horse through the winter. We called this family, Mark and Denise Beckel and their children, and they were interested. After several visits, they decided to buy Savannah. It was pouring down rain the day they came to pick her up. The Beckels had borrowed a two-horse trailer, and with that overcast day, I guess the trailer looked like a dungeon to Savannah. Well, she just wasn't going to get into that trailer. We tried everything: talking sweetly and not so sweetly, putting hay and grain in the trailer, having Bijou next to her to hopefully tell her it was okay (he didn't cooperate!). Finally, after much work Savannah was in and on her way to someone else's farm. It was a good feeling, but also sad. Now what were we supposed to do for a horse for Jeannie?

Since Bijou was the only horse left, he became the family horse and everyone rode him. He didn't give very good rides, though. He seemed to miss bossing Savannah around. He continued to refuse to give Stevie a good ride and even bucked Jeannie off one time. Also, since Savannah was gone, he had to have something else to boss around. His solution was to boss the pregnant cows. He would run them all over the pasture apparently just for the thrill of seeing them run in panic. That did not make me very happy! Those cows were carrying calves that would be very useful on our farm, and as far as I was concerned Bijou was not doing anything very useful on our farm.

The straw that broke the camel's back, however, was when we found out that our three-year-old son, Ben, was terribly allergic to horses. His allergies triggered asthma attacks. That was it! It was time for Bijou to go also. We called the Beckels and asked if they wanted to buy Bijou. They couldn't take him right then, but gave us two or three names of people who might want him. The next person I called was very interested in Bijou. She came out, liked what she saw, and bought him. I told you he was beautiful. I think that helped to sell him so quickly. Bijou left five months after Savannah.

Thus ended another chapter in the saga of Castleberry horses. Will we get more horses? Maybe, as soon as Ben is no longer allergic to them. Will we make the same mistakes? I don't honestly know. I think we are all older and hopefully more mature now than we were then. We certainly won't go into the whole proposition with our eyes closed. We understand now that horses have personalities that we must get to know and respect. I am sure we will spend much time trying to find just the right horses.

Actually, the next horses we get might not be pleasure horses at all. We have toyed with the idea of work horses for quite a few years now. When I say work horses I mean that the horses would do the work that most people use tractors for. Horses would pull plows, rakes, and harrowers. They would pull hay mowers and draw hay wagons. They would haul in logs and pull bobsleds.

In anticipation of future work horses on our farm, during our first summer here we bought several horse drawn implements. We bought a steel-wheeled manure spreader, a disc, a bobsled and a plow. Later I bought a hay mower. All of these items are horse-drawn and in working order, except for the hay mower that I am currently reconditioning.

We also started looking at and learning about draft horses. Again, there are several breeds to choose from. There are heavy breeds like Belgians, Clydesdales, Shires, Percheron, and the Suffolk Punch. There are also smaller breeds like Haflingers and Norwegian Fjords. The magazine we take, *Small Farmers Journal*, is an excellent resource for information about working with draft horses.

Several people in our area raise and train Belgians. These are big, powerful horses. John Lima, a friend who lives about 15 minutes from our house, raises Belgians. One day we took a drive to his farm and stepped out of the car and into the pasture. He called his horses and they came running. I can't describe the incredible power I sensed from those eight Belgians as they got closer. The ground actually shook and trembled. They encircled us and started to eat the grain he had thrown out. I felt small and very insignificant. Yet these magnificent beasts were not mean. They quietly stood there looking at us as we quietly stood there looking at them.

One early fall day I went over to John's to help him work with his horses and thus learn more about them. I remember he was trimming their hooves. He would tie each horse to a hay wagon, and when those huge animals wanted to leave they just walked away, dragging the hay wagon like it was a feather. I was so interested in this hoof trimming that I took a piece of hoof home to show the children what a really big "toenail" looked like. Sad to say, by the time I got home I had forgotten all about that big "toenail." Several days later, while I was on my way to work, I kept smelling a rather unpleasant odor in the car. The first thing I checked was my shoes. I sometimes go to the barn right before I leave for work and then later learn that I brought some manure along. I'll never forget sitting at the front of one of those larger-sized university classrooms while giving a test and smelling something "funny." "Boy, I sure hope that's not me," I thought. When I crossed my legs, it about knocked me over! Since then I have learned to wear one pair of shoes to work, and then change into "school" shoes while I am there. Anyway, it wasn't my shoes this day in the car. I finally realized that the bad smell was coming from that old horse "toenail" that was now rotten. I learned a lesson that I hope won't need repeating!

John Lima also invited me out to his place one winter morning to help hitch and drive his Belgians. I was absolutely amazed at how much the harness and hames weigh for draft horses. It is a very big deal to put it all on correctly (buckle things up the way they are supposed to go and get the lines all straight). After getting them set up, we headed for the field. There was plenty of snow on the ground so there wasn't as much danger of having them run away. I watched him handle the lines and talk to his horses. It was really neat. I was impressed about how they listened to his voice and hand commands. Then he handed me the lines and said, "Now, you drive them." That was a little scary! I said "get up" and they took off. But then I just didn't know what to do. John said, "Talk to them." That sounds simple, doesn't it? But what do you talk about? The weather? The Cubs? How good those oats are back in the barn? I honestly didn't know what to say to them and told John. By now the horses were getting a little nervous because their leader (me) was getting pretty nervous. They started running. I tried to stop them but to no avail. "Pull back a little on their reins. Let them know you are there and in control. Talk to them and tell them to slow down," John shouted over to me. But I couldn't seem to make the horses settle down. Finally, he took the reins from my hand (probably because I looked out of control, which I was!) and stopped them in a few seconds. It is all in knowing what you are doing and having confidence in what you are doing. I had neither! John was very patient with me for which I am thankful.

I wasn't sure I wanted such big horses as Belgians. The other large breeds of draft horses aren't generally found around here but I didn't think I needed to see any more really large horses. What attracted me more were the smaller breeds of draft horses. I wrote to some farms about Norwegian Fjords, but the prices they wanted seemed astronomical to me (like $7,500 for a mare and $3,000-$4,500 for unbroken colts and fillies!). And none of these farms were anywhere near where we live. Then I learned that Arlo and Shirley Peterson had some Haflingers about 30 minutes from our farm and we decided to go and take a look.

When I saw those Haflingers, I felt I had found the right breed for me. They are really small, yet can handle large jobs with ease. Their size makes them seem more manageable. That should increase my self-confidence which would probably help both their performance and mine. Arlo didn't want to sell any of his stock, but he gave me the address of a Haflinger magazine. I placed a want ad in this paper to see what Haflingers sell for. I got several replies and the prices didn't cause my eyes to jump out of my head (mares for $3000-$4200, and teams for $3000-$4000). However, all of the horses for sale were quite a distance from my farm. I didn't feel excited about driving eight hours just to look at a horse that may or may not be what I was looking for. Also, by that time we had found out that Ben was allergic to horses so I knew I couldn't buy any at that time anyway. If God blesses Ben and cures him of his allergies, Haflingers are the breed I will look at most closely.

So, we aren't farming with horses today. That is sad in a way because it seems like a natural thing for us to do. We want to move away from the reliance upon electricity and fuels, we want to be more self-sufficient, and we want to do things on a much slower and smaller scale than the average farmer. The use of draft horses would accomplish most of those goals. We aren't concerned, though, because God has a plan for our lives and He knows best. In the meantime, we as a family are learning more and maturing more, so that if the time ever does come that we can have horses, we will be much better prepared.

Chapter 7
Milking the Family Cow

Who would think of living a self-sufficient lifestyle without a family milk cow lounging around somewhere? And yet, that is exactly the situation on many small farms today. In his excellent book entitled *Grow It!*, Richard Langer introduces his chapter on dairy goats with the statement " . . . while there's nothing wrong with having a cow on your spread, sometimes she's more trouble than she's worth." (p. 191). Apparently cows are bemoaned because they produce more milk than an average family can consume, cows apparently want to have the same person milk them each time, cows' milk is harder for most people to digest than goats' milk, and cows can get tuberculosis while goats cannot. Most of our friends who have a source of milk on their farm own goats, not cows.

And yet, I suppose I must admit right here that I have never had a strong desire to own a goat. Nor am I alone, apparently. One of my goat-owning friends jokes that he is willing to give his goats away, but he charges $5 if the person decides to bring it back! No, goats were not in the master plan for our farming adventure.

I must also admit that having a family milk cow, while appealing to my sense of self-sufficiency, was not something that I totally looked forward to. I had helped some neighbors milk their cows (with milking machines, not by hand) and it seemed like a smelly, toilsome job that had to be done twice a day no matter how you felt or how many biting flies were flying around. It was also apparent to me who would be shoveling the manure and solving problems that would certainly come up.

Then a way suddenly appeared to try out a milk cow, right on our own farm, without making any long-term decisions. No, we didn't dial "Rent a Milk Cow." And we didn't rustle one from our neighbor's farm for a day. Actually it was quite simple.

You see, we had decided that we would like to butcher a cow and get some fresh beef. I learned about a farmer, whom I'll call Jed, who had a big Holstein (black and white) cow that he wanted to get rid of. Jed was currently milking her but she was not producing enough each day to warrant keeping her much longer. Also, the cow had been unable to get pregnant again. Why not buy this cow, milk her for a week or so just to see how we liked it, and then butcher her? Sounded like a perfect setup to us. So that's what we did.

Of course, the obvious problem was how to bring home a 1500 pound animal. For that, Fred Glavan agreed to let us use his stock trailer and Chevy Suburban. He even graciously agreed to drive and help load/unload. The second problem was how we could ever eat a 1500 pound animal. Uncle Jim decided to split the cow with us and help us butcher. With all problems solved we were ready to begin!

Well, not quite. For you see the cow had gotten quite attached to Jed's farm and didn't really want to trot up into the stock trailer. We tried just about everything: coaxing with grain, slapping, pushing, shoving, scaring, talking. One lesson I learned was that it is impossible to make a cow go where you want it to go just by pushing! Finally we attached a rope to the side of the trailer and put it behind her back end. Then by pulling on the rope, pressure was applied to her back side. She seemed a little annoyed at this and decided to move forward so she could turn around and see what was happening back there. As she did, we tightened the rope again. We played this trick long enough to get her into the trailer.

At our farm, we unloaded her and chained her to one of the stanchions. Of course we had to name our new arrival. At that time we didn't have a good system in place for deciding on names for animals, so our cow ended up with a variety of names. Three year-old Ben called her "A Moo." Jeannie and Stevie, already avid readers and knowledgeable about proper names for cows, named her "Blossom." Katie preferred "Patience" (Katie was not with me when I tried to load "Patience" on the trailer; the cow seemed anything but patient to me). Finally, Betsy called her

"Bonnie" (which seemed a little more appropriate when you think of the outlaw couple "Bonnie and Clyde").

We now have a system for naming animals on the farm. The responsibility for naming a new animal rests on the shoulders of a single child. The rule states that he or she can name the animal anything he or she wants. Then, the next animal we acquire is named by the next child in birth order. Over time, every child gets to name the same number of animals. Of course, there is some jealousy at times: "You got to name a cow, all I got to name was a kitten!" Over time it should work out to be fair for everyone.

In preparation for milking A Moo Blossom Patience Bonnie we had purchased a fifty-pound bag of dairy grain. We also read every book we could find on milking and had talked to several people about milking "rules." We were ready! We marched out to the barn and filled her grain bucket with about two pounds of grain. She contentedly started munching her goodies. So far, so good. I sat down on a stool, cleaned the cow's udder really well, and started milking. As I squeezed and pulled, milk started coming out! Boy, this seemed easy.

But as the minutes slowly went by my hands started getting tired and sore. Susie decided to jump in and help. But she too got tired. "The cow's about out of grain," one of the children said. "Well, give her some more," I replied. They obeyed. Then Susie and I decided to milk her at the same time (this is not recommended by any book we had read, but we were getting tired and not a little desperate to milk her out). So, with Susie on one side and me on the other we milked. And milked. And milked. The two of us milked for 1 ½ hours before we quit. It usually takes an experienced person 10-15 minutes to milk a cow. What did we get for our trouble? About 14 ½ pounds of milk (which is about a gallon), sore hands, sore arms, and a cow with a stomachache from eating so much grain.

The next morning we got 11 pounds of milk. On the following milkings our production is painfully recorded in my farm journal: 11 pounds, 13 pounds, 12 pounds, and 14 pounds. After that I quit keeping records. I didn't want to use my tired hand muscles more than necessary! But we did cut the time down. At least some. After a day or so Robin came by to show us how to milk. He kneeled down, and when he started milking the cow, the milk hit the bucket with a strong "SWOOSH! SWOOSH! SWOOSH!" Just watching him milk a real cow right in front of me helped me learn the trick of how and when to squeeze, when to pull and how to bump the udder to get the milk to let down. Now my biggest problem was a lack of hand stamina. I knew how to milk. I just couldn't do it for very long at a time.

After a few days of this we decided that our experiment was over. We knew how to milk, and knew the pros and cons (or so we thought) of owning our own milk cow. So over the next week and a half, we slowly "dried her up" by removing the grain and milking just once a day. She dried up beautifully! I felt I had mastered one skill: if you have a milk cow that you want to stop producing milk, just give me a call.

A year went by. A year in which we purchased powdered organic milk from a natural food coop. It was sure easier than keeping a milk cow. But we couldn't turn that milk powder into cream, cottage cheese, cheese, yogurt, or butter. And we wanted to try doing those things. The thought of fresh homemade butter on a piece of homemade bread just out of the oven (with a slice of homemade cheese) wouldn't go away. We kept telling ourselves that our problem with milking A Moo Blossom Patience Bonnie was just that she was not a family milk cow, so she was harder to hand-milk. She had spent her life as one more cow in a throng of cows at a dairy farm. Now, if we had a *real* family milk cow, things would be different!

We also read more about the breeds of cows that are available. It seems that Holsteins (the black and white ones) are now the most popular for real dairy farms. They give tons of milk but it's not very rich in butterfat. Also they are really big and can have an attitude problem. Jerseys are smaller, give less milk, but their milk contains the most butterfat. Jerseys are supposed to be better natured, also. The other main dairy breeds, which are more rare in this area, include Guernsey, Ayrshire, and

Brown Swiss. These three breeds are pretty much between Jerseys and Holsteins on milk production and butterfat content. Two dual-purpose breeds, meaning they are good for beef or milk, are Milking Shorthorn, and the Red Poll. We decided that we wanted a breed high in butterfat, and that we didn't need tons of production. Jerseys seemed to make sense for us.

It was then that we learned of Molly. Molly was a real family milk cow, and part Jersey at that! She lived her life with a family, and was milked by hand, not machine. She was used to having children around her and seemed content to live on a family farm. Sounded like a perfect situation to us, so we went to take a look at her.

When I saw her, she was tied up in a little milking shed, causing no problems. She was smaller than our first milk cow because she was a light brown Jersey-Guernsey mix. But there was something in her eyes that didn't quite look right to me. Seemed like she had some mischief or something hiding back deep in her brain. Her horns didn't look safe to me. I didn't say anything to Susie about it because her owner was so convinced that she was a good, gentle cow. "My son even crawls under her and she never bothers him!" Of course, she spent her time mostly tied up in the shed. Well, the message sounded good even though the cow didn't quite look right. I fully believed then and do today that what the owner told me was 100% true. Molly had been a great cow for him.

We were impressed with the owners and their claims of gentleness for Molly. But we needed to make sure she was bred back (that means pregnant). The owners had bred her back, artificially, and she was supposed to calf in December (this was early fall). The owners agreed to have a vet check her so we went home and waited for their phone call. A few weeks later we got a rather interesting call. It seems that the artificial insemination hadn't taken, but that she was pregnant by her "son" and was due to calf in March. That set us back a little bit. We were hoping to bring the cow home and just have to feed her for a few months before starting to get milk. Now, we were looking at feeding her for about six months before the milk supply started. We said we would have to think about it.

After a few months of thinking we decided that we would take Molly. I borrowed Fred Glavan's Suburban and stock trailer (are you keeping track of the number of times we have borrowed this?) and headed to Molly's house. I looked her over carefully to make sure everything was okay. I didn't see any bullet holes in her and she was able to walk so I figured she was okay (what else could I look at?). But those eyes, they still had something in them that I couldn't quite figure out. Seemed like her horns had grown a little also. Susie didn't say anything about them though. Oh well, I had the truck and might as well go ahead and take her. She was supposed to be gentle.

We opened the doors to the stock trailer and pointed her in the right direction. Remember that I had not had very much success loading milk cows before. So I was surprised and shocked when Molly just walked up to the trailer, smelled it, and waltzed right in. Maybe this was a good cow after all.

When we got home, I backed the trailer up as close to the barn as I could. Even so, there was still a good sized space between one side of the trailer and the front of the barn which would be big enough for a cow to escape. The state highway was only 150 feet away. "Hey, Stevie," I said, "Grab that 50-foot piece of rope in the barn." He did and I attached one end of the rope to the first support beam in our barn. The other end of the rope was tied securely to the cow's chain around her neck. My thinking was that if she did try to run away, at least she couldn't get more than 50 feet away. When I was satisfied that the rope was all in place and securely tied, I carefully untied the lead rope that had secured her in the trailer on the way home. I held onto the lead rope and hoped that she would know (or at least think) I was still in control.

She looked at me, backed up a little, and then turned around to look at the back of the trailer. Slowly she moved toward the open trailer door and stepped gingerly out. I walked her (that means that she walked me) into the barn and started down the barn aisle toward the stall we had prepared for her. Suddenly something must have snapped in her brain because she started running as hard and as fast as she could toward the back of the barn.

I desperately tried to hold her back with the lead rope but she just dragged me down the aisle. I told her to WHOA! Apparently she hadn't successfully attended any horse training classes in her time and kept on running. I could see nothing but trouble coming. She would run until she took out all of the slack of the rope and then one of two things would happen: (1) She would be jerked off her feet, causing her to crash to the concrete floor, break a leg and/or have a miscarriage of the calf inside her, or (2) she would have so much power, weight and momentum that she would pull down the support beam attached to the other end of the rope, causing the roof to cave in on us. What actually happened was a variation of number 1. When she reached the end of her rope, she came crashing down and nearly choked herself to death. But she didn't break a leg and she didn't miscarry the calf. I felt very blessed. I also felt like screaming in pain, because I had been holding onto her halter the entire time she was careening down the aisle, without any gloves on.

Was this crazy behavior "the thing" I had noticed in her eyes? And now, were her eyes trying to give me a new message? "Just give me 100 feet of rope, bub, and then see what I'll do!" Well, I wasn't interested in seeing what she would do with more rope, so we decided to let her out with the other five cows. She took over immediately! She pushed and shoved and generally got her way about everything. If Molly could speak English, the airwaves would probably have been filled with the following: "You guys thirsty? Well, if there's any left when I'm done you can have it! Hungry? We'll see if there is any hay left worth a dime when I'm through! And hey, you! Yeah, you! I don't want you standing there, so move out, bub!" Her supposed gentleness didn't seem to be flowing forth from a well of plenty.

When I grew up, in Tennessee, we still had chain gangs of convicts which would work on the roads. Actually, I notice chain gangs are coming back in vogue these days in Alabama and Arizona. Experts are finally realizing that idleness tends to breed more violence and create more tension in prisons. That's why all inmates at Duluth's Federal Prison Camp have jobs. Oh, the Duluth inmates also have cable TV, a gymnasium, weight room, handball and racquetball courts, pool tables, a movie house, musical instruments, and until recently Haagen-Dazs ice cream and a six lane bowling alley for the 500 inmates. Guess I would hope for Duluth over Alabama if I was heading to the slammer.

Anyway, these chain gang guys (why were no gals ever in chain gangs?) were all serving time in the county jail and had to work on the roads. They wore black and white striped clothes with sweat pulsing from every pore. Each convict had a heavy chain attached to both legs to keep them from running away, although it didn't seem necessary with a burly guard watching over them cradling a short barreled 12 gauge shotgun! As they were moved from one worksite to another, they were transported in a small cage built on the back of a work truck. I always thought these must be the toughest and meanest guys on the face of the earth. When they would work on the road in front of our house, we would run into the house, shaking with terror, and peer out the windows at them. Sometimes a convict would look over at where we were peeking out, which would scare us even more. As a little boy I always wondered why the county didn't issue a warning that the chain gang was coming to our area. You know, maybe a loudspeaker attached to the top of a police car, blaring, "Warning! Get your children off the streets! Lock your doors and windows! The chain gang is coming!"

Since Molly had a chain around her neck, I often thought of her in the same light as those chain gang men. Boy, she was tough and she was mean. Her horns commanded respect from everybody, man and beast. Time for a new loudspeaker, perhaps attached to the top of a tractor, blaring, "Warning! Cows get your calves out of the pasture! Lock your gates and barn doors! Chain gang Molly is coming!"

Even though she was tough, the other cows survived the winter living with her. In early spring, the other cows had their calves. Molly sometimes pushed the new calves around which didn't endear her to my heart. Then March rolled around. Time for Molly to calve. Only, she didn't.

Maybe she is just a little bit late. It does happen. While we waited, we spent our time strategizing how we would milk Molly. We decided to let her calf nurse as much as it wanted. We would then milk Molly once a day and get all the milk we needed for our family. In that way, it wouldn't be necessary to worry so much about milking on a strict schedule (meaning we could take small or long trips if we wanted to) and her calf would get all the milk it needed. We had read of people doing this so we weren't out of our minds. It sure sounded like a good plan to us.

April rolled around. Still, no calf. I was getting even less happy with Molly. In May, our family took a long, three week trip down south. Wouldn't you know it, while we were gone, she had her calf. A little bull calf that we named George (more about him in an upcoming chapter). Now, how were we supposed to start getting Molly used to being milked by us when we were 900 miles away?

When we returned from our trip, we were exhausted. The grass had grown about 1 ½ feet while we were gone. There were chores everywhere that needed doing. One top priority was to start milking Molly, but it had been a *long* time since she had been milked. It had even been a long time since she was in a barn. And in these last few weeks, she had enjoyed living outside in the open, playing with her calf and doing what she wanted to do. Thus, our attempts at coaxing her into the barn to be milked were met with, not surprisingly, reluctance. That's putting it mildly. She wasn't going to come in and be milked without a fight to the death. My patience with her was pretty well used up and I almost looked forward to a "fight to the death." Especially with the rifle in my hand.

We did get her in the barn. We even finally got her tied up to the stanchion that we had reserved just for her. But she was not happy. Her calf ran around the barn bleating and probably sending out secret cow messages like "Mommy, save me from this place! I think I am going to die if you don't come over here and nurse me right now!" Molly sensed the urgency of these messages because she kept turning back and looking at her calf about every 10 seconds. We probably should have kept the calf out of the barn, but when we tried that, she seemed worse.

The first thing you do before milking a cow is to clean the udder because it can be very caked with manure and other cruddy things. As you can imagine, she wasn't thrilled with this part of the deal. Then when we put a bucket under her and started to milk her, she suddenly became interested in stopping our little plans all together. She began to move around, swishing her tail from side to side slapping us in the face. She would back up, let you get all set up (sitting in front of her back leg leaning far under her to milk), and then suddenly move forward. This can be scary! It is kind of like crawling under the car near the back tire and then having the car suddenly start rolling toward you. You either get out of the way or you are going to get squished!

When we got a little milk in our bucket, Molly would suddenly kick the pail with her back leg, spilling it or splashing some out, or just knocking some good old manure from her hooves into the bucket. It was frustrating. I am not generally a patient man and didn't become more patient working with her. In fact, she pushed me near to my breaking point. I think Molly was really enjoying herself.

On top of these problems, we still weren't very good milkers. Even though I had been practicing in the bathtub for about a year (by squirting water through my hands, trying to hit the ceiling) my hands still got tired easily. The same was true for everyone else who milked. Thus, it took us a long time to milk Molly out, a fact that didn't make her any less irritable.

I could have called for help from our friends and neighbors who knew all about milking cows. But I just didn't want to bother them with what I thought was our problem. Susie and I decided to move to more extreme measures. We decided to hobble Molly's back feet. That would keep her from being able to move forward and backwards and keep her from turning over the bucket. Since we didn't own a pair of "official" hobbles, we rigged some up with baling twine.

We tied her legs up pretty securely and walked out of the

barn for a few minutes. "Let's just give her a few minutes to feel those hobbles and let her learn who's boss around here," I said. When we returned in a few minutes, there stood Molly, hobbles on the floor, looking at us as if to say, "You're not as tough as I thought! I'm going to have lots of fun ruining your day!"

Then we remembered that someone had said if you hold a cow's tail high into the air, they can't kick you. In fact they can't move. Or at least that is what we thought we remembered someone saying. We grabbed her tail, but Molly saw where this was heading and let out a pretty good kick in our direction. Since no one wanted to be in the direct line of her kicks while holding her tail, we decided to just tie her tail to the stanchion. And, while we are at it, why not try hobbling her again? So we tied her tail with baling twine and hobbled her back feet with another good long piece of baling twine.

It did no good. She was able to get out of her hobbles. And the tail tied to the stanchion just made her totally uncontrollable! It was time to bring in some help. The next day we called Todd who said he would be happy to teach us how to milk a cow.

Todd came over and stood in the aisle at the front of the barn. "Go ahead and do what you have been doing and I'll see what happens. If you're doing something wrong, I'll let you know." We suggested that he move near a pole for protection but he didn't seem worried. The back barn door was opened and there stood Molly. Have you ever taken a car to the repair shop because, say, the wipers didn't work and then when you showed the mechanic, the wipers worked beautifully? Well, that is pretty much what happened here. Molly joyfully walked down the aisle and headed for her stanchion. She had never done that before! Todd, who has a great sense of humor, looked at us like were crazy or something and said, "Okay, is this the bad habit you were telling me about?" He got her in the stall, milked her, and she behaved much better than she had for us. She still wasn't perfect though. Todd gave us a few pointers and suggested that part of the problem might be the flies bothering Molly. We thanked Todd and he left.

After spraying Molly with fly spray, we found that she did

act better. Not perfect, no sir. But better. The only problem then was that the milk tasted just like fly spray. The butter tasted like fly spray. Now, we had gotten this cow partly because we wanted fresh, wholesome, organic-type milk and milk products. But fly spray doesn't exactly taste fresh, wholesome, or organic. We looked at the calendar and realized that we would have to spray Molly about 4 ½ months out of the year. That means that about half the time we were milking her, the milk and milk products would taste yucky. No good! We also learned that we could buy fresh raw milk from an area farmer straight out of the bulk tank. Since his milk hadn't been homogenized, we could still make butter with it. Oh, and it didn't taste like fly spray either. We tried some of his milk and decided that this approach was the answer to our problems.

What were we going to do with Molly? We decided to sell her and keep her calf. We put an ad in the free local paper and got only one call. The people came out and looked Molly over. We were very honest and told them all about her antics and behaviors. They didn't seem really worried about it and decided to buy her. I couldn't believe it! We sold our problem cow Molly and became friends with some really neat people, Jim and Fran Yadon, in the process. Jim took Molly home and milked her successfully. Later, he did use a small mechanical milker, which milked her out much quicker than we could by hand and that probably helped. I also think his success was due to his lack of fear of failure and that he really did know what he was doing. We all won. He got a cow giving good clean milk (no problem with fly-spray-tasting milk if you use a mechanical milker), and we got to keep the calf.

After Molly left the farm, Susie said, "You know, there was something in her eyes even before we bought her that made me wonder about her. She never really looked gentle to me." I couldn't believe what I was hearing! Why hadn't Susie confided her thoughts to me before we bought Molly? On the other hand, why had I not told Susie my thoughts either? We decided that in the future we would be really honest and open with each other before buying another animal. That open communication should help us keep the same kind of problem from occurring again. Well, at least it might help.

Maybe Richard Langer was right. Maybe a milk cow is more trouble than she's worth. I don't know. All I know is that, for our family at this time, we aren't interested in experimenting once again with a family milk cow. And no, I am still not interested in a dairy goat, no matter how much our friends try to convince us.

I believe if we ever do try a dairy cow again in the future, we will probably buy a young heifer, get her used to us, and then breed her back. If the cow likes and knows us, it may make a difference. I also think we will invest in one of the small mechanical milkers. Of course, we will also not be so reluctant to ask for help next time if we experience difficulties! After all, that is what friends are for.

Chapter 8
Beef Ranching on a Small Scale

Susie and I had wanted to start raising our own beef because then we would know what was in our food (and maybe even more important, what <u>wasn't</u> in the food-like drugs, chemicals, etc.). Also, we're a large family and the price of beef at the grocery store isn't that cheap. Raising our own should save us a few bucks. We got into raising our own beef in a rather roundabout way as I described in the first chapter. Todd-the-cow was our very first beef-on-the-hoof that we owned.

Our experience of bottle-feeding Todd was very positive. The children had fun doing it and Todd seemed to enjoy it too! Beef cows seemed like a good thing. So when Uncle Jim called a few months later and asked if we had room in our pasture for his two calves, Spot and Brownie, we said "sure!" Jim's pasture fences weren't too good and he was getting tired of rounding up the wayward cows. Even though we wouldn't be bottle-feeding them because they were too old, we still looked forward to having a "herd" at our place. I have noted the antics of these three bull calves, Todd, Spot, and Brownie earlier in this book.

One of our first major tasks was to dehorn the cows. This can be done several different ways, but basically involves burning them off, cutting them, or applying a chemical paste which takes them off. Dehorning needs to be done correctly or the cows can grow new horns. The Bitners came over and dehorned Todd by burning them off. However, the horns of Spot and Brownie were too big to burn off. So, Todd (the human, not Todd-the-cow) was kind enough to call the local high school agriculture teacher, who came out with a tool that looked like a giant pair of fingernail clippers and cut them off. Dehorning, no matter how you do it, is not a fun job. It can even be hard to get cows dehorned because you really shouldn't do it, at least up here where we live, in the months that don't have an "r" in them (May, June, July, August). During these months, if you dehorn, you run the risk that flies will lay their larvae in the wounds, which can be a really messy situation.

Once we had all of our calves steered and dehorned we were able to just watch them play and eat grass in the pasture. Raising beef animals seemed like a neat thing to do. As late fall approached, we decided that we wouldn't mind having another calf to bottle feed.

We learned where Uncle Jim got his little Jersey bull calves and gave the farmers a call. These were dairy farmers and had little use for bull calves. They said that they expected several cows to calve at any time. But every time we called them, we learned that the latest cows had given birth to heifer (female) calves, something the farmers could and would use to build their herd. Finally, in late October, we got a call that a bull calf had been born and that we should come and get him. Our entire family went to pick him up. He was so cute and only cost us $35! Everyone agreed he looked just like a little deer. So guess what we named him? No, not Fawn. Star. Because he had a star in the middle of his forehead.

We put Star in the back of the van (with plastic under hay for bedding) and drove the hour and a half home. Star was good on the way home. Of course just to add to the excitement of the trip, we heard, "Hey Dad! I think he's going to . . . Yep. There it comes. Right on the floor . . . " That didn't keep the children from riding back there with Star all the way home. Even when it was time to pass out the food we had brought along (it was getting late and we hadn't eaten), the children just ate their sandwiches in the back with the calf! Children are different, aren't they?

When we finally got home, Star was placed in the 8' x 16' calf pen that we had built out of scrap lumber lying around the barn. Again the children had so much fun bottle-feeding a calf. This time I made sure to dehorn him at two months old. Raising our own beef was working out wonderfully. So much so that we decided we should start building our own herd of beef cows. We could eat what we needed and sell the rest as drug-free beef. We wanted to get into just one breed and stick to it.

When trying to choose a beef breed, we consulted a lot of sources. A popular breed around here is the Polled Hereford. One advantage of this breed is obvious right away - that is if you know what "polled" means. Polled means that this breed will not grow any horns. This was a real plus because, as I've already noted, dehorning cattle is no fun. Another good trait of Herefords is that they are good grazers. They know how to find food.

Angus was another possibility because many people up here raise them. Angus, also naturally polled, are hardy animals. One drawback is that their fat tends to marble, meaning that the fat mixes in with the lean meat. The result is a more tender piece of meat, but with more fat content. That trait is not a good one for me, since I am trying to reduce my fat and cholesterol intake. Another drawback is that we have been told Angus can be mean. We don't know if that is true, but for someone not especially gifted with the ability to handle animals, that was all I needed to hear.

There are many other breeds of beef cattle to choose from. Some others that we have in this area include Shorthorn and an occasional Brahma. One breed, however, that really took our fancy was the Scotch Highland breed. Scotch Highland were particularly noteworthy for several characteristics: they produce naturally leaner beef, they are good mothers, they have very long hair which reduces problems associated with flies and insects and keeps them warmer in the winter, and they gain more weight on less feed. One disadvantage is that they have long horns. Horns can be cut off, however.

We were so taken by the literature on the Scotch Highland breed that we felt we should start raising them. But where to begin? I didn't know anyone raising them in our area. One day I mentioned to a neighbor about my interest in Scotch Highland cattle and she said she knew a farm that raised them several hours south of us. To make a long story short, we contacted this farm and found they had a newborn bull calf that they planned on selling as soon as it was weaned. If we wanted to reserve it all we had to do was send in a nonrefundable $50 deposit. Susie and I talked about it and decided that we would take it. I sent the $50 and received a receipt in the mail. The bull's name was Mork (his mother's name was Mindy).

As the months passed, Mork grew and grew. Soon it was time to pick up the calf. Only now it weighed several hundred pounds and we learned that, on a per pound basis, this calf was going to cost us more than we would have to pay for a full-grown, ready-to-butcher cow of another breed. Suddenly we wondered why we had even reserved this calf in the first place. What did we hope to do with it? We couldn't start a herd with him because we didn't have any female Scotch Highland cows on the place. We didn't really want to raise a bull (they can get mean) without assurance that soon we would have a heifer to breed him to. And we didn't have any prospects of securing a Scotch Highland heifer. If we just wanted him for his beef, why not buy a ready-to-butcher cow for the same money and save ourselves the headaches of raising this calf for another year before butchering?

In the end, we decided to let the farm keep Mork and our $50 deposit. Sometimes it makes sense to cut your losses early. Of course, it would have been better to recognize our mistake earlier, and thus save ourselves the $50. The funny thing is, we have since learned that a farm raises Scotch Highland cattle about 10 minutes from our farm! Thus, another lesson we learned was to ask more people about things before jumping into something.

Late that fall, a neighbor who lives about four miles from us gave us a call. We knew her from buying some horse-drawn equipment. She stated that she was selling her farm and cows and asked us to pass the word on to whoever might be interested in buying. "What kind of cows do you have?" Susie asked. "Polled Herefords," was the reply. Hmmm. Interesting. We had been thinking about slowly building a herd of polled Herefords and had even gone so far as to look at some for sale. We learned that her's were bred back (meaning they were pregnant) and due to calf in the spring. The price was very reasonable.

We drove out to look at the cows. Once again, they looked like cows. No bullet holes and all seemed to be standing without crutches. Looked good to me. After thinking about it awhile, we decided to buy two cows from her.

"Hello, Fred? This is Steve. Can we borrow your stock trailer to pick up some cows? . . .Thanks." And so the saga of borrowing the Glavans' trailer continued. It was very cold the day we went to pick up the cows. They had not been in a barn for a long time, and Jim, the owner's son, had quite a bit of trouble coaxing the first one in before we arrived. When we pulled up in the trailer he said, "We'll get this first one loaded up and then we can run the other one into the barn and load her up." Sounded like an easy deal to me. There seems to be an unwritten rule that says that whoever is selling you something is responsible for loading it safely into your trailer.

My two oldest children and I opened up the trailer door and the barn door and waited for the cow to march in. But she was not so sure she wanted to enter that trailer. In fact, she wasn't too sure she even wanted to be in the barn. Jim tried pushing her and steering her in the direction of the open trailer door. Just when we thought things were moving along fine, the cow would suddenly veer off and stampede into something lying in the barn. Jim was afraid that the children, peering around from behind the trailer door, might be scaring the cow, so we asked them to hop in the truck. Jim and I made another attempt to coax the cow into the trailer, using grain this time. Again, at the last minute she veered off.

"Oh no, she's heading for the fencing. Not the fencing!" Jim yelled, as the cow crashed into several rolls of fencing. I guess he could picture, as well as I could, a cow getting all tangled up in fencing and barbed wire. What a mess! Well, the cow freed herself from the fencing and we tried to move her along again. This time Jim had a big stick to prod her from behind. The result was that the cow veered off in another direction.

"Oh no! Not the riding lawnmower!" he shouted, as the cow quickly ran over the top of his mower. You could hear metal crunching as the 1000+ pound animal "waded" though the lawn-mower.

Jim had had about enough of this foolishness. He grabbed a pitchfork and firmly nudged the cow (with the handle, not the forks!). This caused her no little anger and the cow moved over to the other side of the barn, heading toward the front. Now she was picking her way through the rubble lying all over the place until she came to a big box with electrical wires hanging out of it.

"NO! NO!" shouted Jim. "Not the water pump!" But the cow apparently didn't understand English too well, or pretended not to, and kept on walking. She bumped the big box, knocking it to the ground. As she did, a "Sssssshhhhh" sound started coming from that area. When I looked closely, I could see that the cow had knocked over a little insulated "house" covering the pipes leading up from the well below. The "Sssssshhhhh" sound was water running out of the now broken pipe sticking up out of the ground.

Jim muttered something like, "I'm supposed to be at work in half an hour. The water line's broken, and that's the water supply to the house, too." He was not too happy. Actually, neither was I. I was beginning to wonder what kind of wild beasts I was buying here.

Jim said he was sorry that things didn't work out well, and could he please just load them up and deliver them right to our farm. I said "sure" and the children and I left. Actually, we left his farm, and since we had the Glavan's trailer, drove over and picked up Molly, a cow I have already told you about.

In about a week Jim called and said they would deliver our cows if we were ready for them. Soon a huge stock trailer pulled up and backed expertly to our pasture. Several men got out to help (Jim was taking no chances this time that anything could go wrong). Jim told me that to get them loaded into the trailer easier, he had built a sort of fence on both sides of the center barn aisle. The only place the cows could go was into the trailer. We unloaded the cows and they gave us no problems whatsoever as they got used to their new home.

About that time I went to the feed store to buy some things.

I told Phyllis, the manager: "We got some new polled Herefords. I need some of that grain you feed cows that you are going to milk." "You're not going to milk those Herefords are you?" she asked with a surprised look on her face. "Oh, no," I said laughing, "the grain is for Molly, our new milk cow." I suppose it wouldn't have surprised Phyllis if I *had* planned on milking the Herefords. I've probably provided her with many hours of fun since I rarely have a clue what I need to ask for. When I run in to buy some feed for my chickens, she says, "What kind? Game bird starter, pullet grower, pullet layer, or what?" I just can't seem to keep it all straight in my head so I usually just say something like, "You know. That junk you feed them right before you kill them." It is so nice to have someone helpful and honest like Phyllis. She could have "taken me to the cleaners" in my ignorance, yet she always only sells me what I really need. Several times, she has saved me money by saying "You know, Steve, you could get by with just using . . . instead of buying . . ." Yes, there are still honest people in this world!

We decided to name the two polled Herefords Daisy and Clover. Daisy is a little fatter and taller than Clover. In the spring, both cows gave birth to heifers, a great thing since we were trying to increase our herd size! The births went great. We didn't even know what was going on until we spotted the new calves in the pasture next to their mammas.

We, again as a family, named the new calves Petal and Leaf. I was so excited by our new additions that I put up streamers and a birth announcement on my university office door. One of the announcements read: IT'S A GIRL! Name: Petal, Mother: Daisy, Weight: 110 pounds, Length: 39", Height: 31". Can you believe that one of my students actually said, "Hey, congratulations on the birth of your new baby! That makes six for you guys, doesn't it?" I think if Susie ever gave birth to a 110-pound baby, the whole world would know it! It helped me understand why some students just don't do well in college. They aren't really paying attention.

The new calves didn't cause any real problems for us. They stayed right next to their mothers and nursed when they wanted to. They were so frisky, running around like little puppies. The only trouble we had was when one would get separated from her mother by crawling through a small hole in the fence. I also put up an electric fence about that time to separate the pasture into smaller paddocks. This is supposed to be good for the pasture. Well, it's not good for baby calves which get separated by that electric fence from their mothers. When that happens the calf and mamma will just look at each other and bawl. I have had to get up in the middle of the night and reunite the two lost souls. It's not something I long to do, but it beats not being able to sleep the rest of the night. Of course, I always wake Susie up and tell her I am going. I know she wants to know.

Those calves sure grew fast. It was amazing to see how much faster they grew, drinking their mamma's milk, than the calves we had raised by bottle feeding. Mamma's milk is simply best! The following year, both cows gave birth to bull calves. Katie named one bull calf "Snowflake" and Betsy named the other "Blizzard." Strange names for calves by most standards, but perfectly acceptable under our rules of naming animals. The rule is simple: the child whose turn it is to name an animal can name that animal *anything*. In case you're wondering, the children don't get to name our little human babies!

I have told you about our beef cows but haven't shared with you all it takes to raise them. The equipment and supplies needed to raise beef are pretty minimal. First, you need a source of clean water. For this, I invested in a 100-gallon rubber stock watering tank. It is oblong and about 3 feet wide x 5 feet long x 2 feet tall. These things are nice because when the water freezes in the winter it won't rupture or dent the tank. Also, they won't rust. Only problem is that it is a little too tall for young stock to drink from; that is unless you keep it filled to the top several times a day. So we do.

You also need some way to feed the cows hay when they have no pasture. You could just throw some out on the ground, but if you do, after the cows are full they will just lay on it and spread manure all over it. At first I used a big old metal stock tank that had the bottom rusted out of it and just filled it with three or four bales of hay. This worked well for a few cows, but became less acceptable as the number of animals increased. The other drawback is that we had to refill it every day with more hay. After a couple of years, I decided to buy a large round-bale hay holder which will hold one round bale or 22 square bales. This is great because we only have to refill it every five or six days.

Of course you also need the hay itself. Up here we feed our cows hay from about the first of October to the middle of May. This takes about 100 bales per full grown cow, although the amount they eat depends on the severity of the winter. I have an arrangement with my neighbor, who cuts my 25 acre hayfield and we split the hay (it's helpful to have a large hayfield on any farm you buy). The only thing I buy for my cows is a mineral block which includes all the salt and minerals that they need. I don't need to buy any grain because I don't feed it to my cows (and the meat is not tough).

Raising beef cows has been fairly easy. But the real goal of raising them is to eventually butcher them, the subject of the next chapter.

Chapter 9
Butchering the Beef

Warning: As the title so cleverly suggests I am going to describe butchering cows in this chapter. If you had rather not read about killing animals, please skip to the next chapter.

I've had the experience of butchering six cows of my own and helping with another one. Before I moved on the farm, I had never butchered anything in my life. I didn't hunt and basically didn't kill things to eat (someone else had killed all of my beef, chicken, etc. for me, like the butcher shops and grocery stores). I had a lot to learn. Thankfully there were many good friends and books that helped. I'll share with you some of the incidents from my feeble attempts at butchering and a little about what I've learned. It's not my goal to teach you completely how to do it in this short section, though. I would recommend that you get help from a friend the first time, and read whatever books you can find on the subject (see the *Recommended Reading List* at the end of this book for some suggestions).

The first cow that I butchered was A Moo Blossom Patience Bonnie, the cow I described in my chapter on milking. Early one cold, cold, cold morning, Robin and Uncle Jim (the co-owner of A Moo etc.) arrived in my driveway. Jim was carrying his deer rifle and an assortment of wicked looking knives. Robin hopped out with his assortment of deadly looking knives and a saw. I placed a chain high up in a tree, secured my own assortment of lethal knives, and had buckets standing by. Let the fun begin!

First, we had to get the cow from the barn to the tree. We could have sent a written invitation, but leading her there with grain sounded like a better idea. Only the cow didn't really want to go outside in that cold, cold wind. Robin knew just how to wrap the rope around her nose and make her move forward. When we got under "the tree" we tied her up to keep her from running away. Uncle Jim then raised his deer rifle and pulled the trigger. The cow dropped to the ground instantly, I stood there in shock, but Robin moved forward quickly and deeply slit the throat from ear to ear so it could bleed out. We were cold and this would take a little time, so we decided to run inside the barn for a few minutes. As we were standing there talking, I decided to make good use of this down time. That's just like me; I'm a Type A personality to the core. I picked up a pitchfork to move some of A Moo's recent manure. Well, something didn't work just right because that simple move "threw my back" and about made me double over with pain. Great! Here I am supposed to handle my share of the heavy work of butchering my first cow and I can hardly move without pain!

After a few minutes, we walked (actually, I slowly and painfully plodded) out of the barn to see if the cow was through bleeding. To our amazement, the cow was up on all four knees rocking back and forth! It was a little scary. "I've never seen anything like that before!" exclaimed Robin, a veteran of many butcherings in his lifetime. Uncle Jim shot her again and she dropped, dead this time. What we later learned is that Jim had shot her where he normally shoots a goat (from behind, right below an ear). This is a different place than where you shoot a cow (for a cow, you draw an imaginary line from each ear to the opposite eye and aim where the lines cross in front).

The next step was to remove the hide. This is not complicated, just hard work. That hide has a tendency to want to stay just where it is, thank you very much! So your job is to cut it away, without cutting off the meat. Removing the hide is eased by raising the cow into the air. I do this with the help of a winch (commonly called a come-along) attached to a chain up in the tree. The come-along is attached to a 2 x 4 board that is wedged in the cow's back leg joints. I try to keep the hide from getting too dirty, because I sell it. I have gotten from $8 - $20 for my hides from the feed store.

After removing the hide, I cut the head off and degut the cow. This is where you want to go easy, so as not to rupture something icky inside! You basically make an incision at the top middle of the cow's belly (remember that the cow is hanging upside down) and slowly rip downward (toward the head). It's easy at the beginning, but as you get about halfway down, the stomachs (remember the cow has four of them!) and intestines start to want to flop out. So you have to kind of hold them in while you continue cutting. I can't emphasize enough the value of having an expert with you the first couple of times you do this. When you get near the bottom you can't hold them back and they come flopping out. It is amazing the size and weight of all this stuff! If you know what you're doing you can even use this as a time to explain animal physiology to your children. I'll never forget watching Robin lie on the frozen ground, trying to blow air into a cow's lung to show the children how the lungs expand and contract.

After the guts are removed, you are basically looking at two "sides" of beef ready to be cut up. For this cow, we cut the animal in half from top to bottom, since Jim owned one half. Next came the cutting into steaks, roasts, stew meat and, of course, hamburger. One advantage of butchering your own beef is that you can decide how lean to make your cuts. We make ours superlean, even more lean than the leanest cuts you can get from the store.

After cutting and wrapping the steaks, roasts, and stew meat and putting them in the freezer, we drove to a local butcher with the hamburger cuts. Here I learned another lesson: If you take your meat to a butcher to be ground, don't carry it in plastic garbage bags. These kinds of bags are designed to break down and may leave some of those chemicals in your meat. Instead use five gallon plastic pails with lids which you can get from any bakery for a dollar or so. The butcher ground the hamburger up for us, although it took several days for him to get to our order and it cost us around 20¢ a pound.

That night we decided to try some of our beef. I whistled as I put some of the best steaks on the grill, happily cooking them to perfection. When we sat down at the table and said grace, we were all grinning, waiting expectantly for that first, perfect bite. That first bite was tough! So were the second and the third and the fourth. In fact, all of the steak was tough! What was wrong?

Later we learned that the roasts were tough. The stew meat was tough. The hamburger was okay, but that had been ground twice. We figured that the problem was the fact that the cow had used her muscles so much right when she died (remember how she rocked up on all fours after we had shot her?). That, coupled with the fact that we didn't grain the cow or cure the beef. I'm afraid we ended up grinding most of that cow for hamburger meat.

With my second butchering experience, Todd-the-cow, we made sure to shoot him in the right place. He was easily led to the tree, following closely a bucket of grain I was carrying. The other cows watched the whole process. They saw him eat the grain and then get shot. Since I still had some grain, I took it over to the cows. Would they be afraid of it after seeing that Todd apparently lost his life because of that very same grain? Cows aren't that smart. They pushed and shoved each other to see which would get the rest of that prize grain.

We had also decided that we would rather grind our own beef and had purchased a hand meat grinder for this purpose. The grinder proved to be very hard to turn, but the result was still hamburger! The meat from Todd was better than A Moo's meat, though still a bit on the tough side.

Brownie was the third cow I butchered and his meat was more tender than either of the first two. However, it still seemed a little tough to me. Should I be graining my cows for the last few months like the commercial farms did? I didn't want to for several reasons. First, I didn't want the expense. Second, I didn't want the extra fat that it put into the meat, fat that I didn't need for my health. Third, the grain you buy isn't organic and you can never be sure what they put in it or what pesticides/herbicides were used when growing the grain.

When we butchered Star, which was my fourth cow to butcher, I decided to let the back half (the two back legs and muscles attached to them) age for a few days. I hung it up in my wood working shop, fully expecting it to be carried away by mice or having it turn into black, deadly cruddy meat. Neither happened. It stayed below freezing in the shop during that time so I covered the hanging carcass with an old sheet and a piece of plastic to keep it from drying out or getting freezer burn. That meat was the most tender and tasty beef that we had ever turned out on our farm. I had hit on a solution!

The fifth cow I butchered was one that we bought as a full-grown steer. Uncle Jim had called and wanted to know if we wanted to go halves on a cow again. They were out of meat, but didn't have room in their freezer for a whole cow. Sure, why not. Even though we had a little beef left, we would be running out before too long. Jim contacted a farmer friend of ours, Dan Siler, who delivered the Holstein steer to our farm. We didn't bother officially naming the steer because he was going to be killed in a few days, but I'll refer to him as Siler (but remember, I'm not talking about Dan when I do, I'm referring to the steer!).

Siler was a big steer and full of energy. We started feeding him grain to get him ready to take his walk to the tree. He seemed very interested in eating grain, so we expected no difficulties.

I mentioned to one of my college students, Todd Graf, that I would be butchering a steer in a few days. "Can I come and watch?" he asked. Actually, I have had a number of college students ask to help me butcher. They have a curiosity about the whole process, which has been carefully hidden from most people. It's kind of like a funeral director's job. The whole process of preparing a body for burial is something that most of us know nothing about. Now, I'm not suggesting that we all hop in our cars and take a field trip to the mortuary, but it does seem strange that we have so shielded ourselves almost completely from death in this culture. That is not the way it used to be in this country, nor is it in other countries today. For one reason or another, we have decided that we would rather not know certain things. Personally, I think that makes us less able to handle things like death or dying, because it seems so alien to us.

Anyway, I said, "Sure, Todd, you can come out and watch." When he asked what it would be like, I tried to present a very honest and realistic picture. "It's basically very easy," I said. "We lead the cow out to a tree by holding grain in front of it. When it gets in position, we shoot it, slit its throat, and let it bleed out. Then we skin it, gut it, and cut it up. It is really no big deal and nothing much ever happens out of the ordinary. It could get pretty dull, but you're welcome to come if you want to." Todd said he wanted to.

The night before butchering day it was very cold. They were predicting wind chills on the following day in the minus 20 degrees F. range. "Do you still want to kill tomorrow?" I asked as I called Jim. "Sure, we might as well. It could always just get colder. It's February you know," was Jim's reply.

It was cold that morning! But true to his word, Todd Graf showed up. In a few minutes Uncle Jim pulled up with all four of his boys. Even though it was cold, at least it looked like we had plenty of help. When we got all of the equipment ready and the come-along attached to the chain in the tree, it was time to bring out Siler. I gave Jim my gun, and walked into the barn. For some strange reason, no one came in with me. I got a huge scoop of grain, put it in his bucket, and opened the gate to Siler's pen.

Opening the gate. A simple, single act, but one that can have momentous outcomes. Like what happened during the very first week I owned my brand spanking new 1979 Honda Accord. Susie's parents had given me a CB radio and I was trying to see if it would install easily in my new car. The stick shift was in the way, so I pulled it down, putting the car in neutral. Then the hand brake was in the way. The only solution was to lower the brake handle, disengaging the emergency brake. I looked the situation over carefully and pretty much decided that it would be too much trouble to install the CB. To be honest, I didn't want to have to drill any holes in my new car. Having satisfied my curiosity, I stepped out of the car and went into the house. About two minutes later we heard this muffled sort of bump. Wondering what that could be, my dad looked out the front window. "Uh oh, Steve!" he said. "You better come here." I walked to the window and looked out. There was my shiny new car, in the neighbor's deep ditch across the road. I ran outside, hoping that the damage would be insignificant. Not so. I had big-time rear end damage and the frame was even bent. Releasing the emer-

gency brake. A simple, single act with disastrous consequences.
Well, now I opened Siler's pen. Another simple, single act.

He came out all right, but he had no interest in the grain. He
had been looking at the chickens across from his pen for a few
days and just had to run over and smell their pen. Satisfied with
that, he then trotted past me (and the grain) and headed for the
open barn door. I have already told you that it is impossible to
stop a full-grown cow just by pulling on it, so I let him walk out.
As I, too, walked out of the front door, I glanced over to the tree
where Siler was supposed to be heading.

There stood one of the funniest sights I have ever seen. In a
long, straight line, solemnly stood Uncle Jim, Morgan, Allen,
Michael, Nathan, Stevie, Jeannie, and Todd. No one moved. No
one twitched. What a serious looking crew! It looked sort of like
an execution squad or something. Uncle Jim was holding the
rifle in a "ready position," one hand on the stock and one on the
barrel, just like you've seen SWAT team members hold their
rifles. And they all just stood there. Siler was obviously misbe-
having, walking aimlessly in the farm yard, and they all just stood
there! I would have laughed out loud, except for the fact that
Siler suddenly started running wildly around the farm yard.

He kicked up his heels and started bucking and charging
everywhere. If you've ever seen a champion bucking bull at a
rodeo you'll have a pretty good idea of what I'm talking about.
Just for fun, Siler even threw in some snorting and bellowing as
he flung himself around the yard. We had a real rodeo going
there. The execution squad remained motionless. Not a smile or
a frown. I couldn't believe it.

Siler spotted my pile of wood ashes (we heat our house with
firewood) and headed for it lickety split. Don't ever let someone
tell you that a big animal can't run fast. It just isn't so! He
smelled the ashes and then started eating them like there was no
tomorrow (for him actually there *was* no tomorrow, but he didn't
know that yet). I was afraid his eating all of those ashes would
somehow mess up his meat. That was not likely, but you have to
remember that my brain wasn't working too well at that moment.
So, I shooed him away. He was more than happy to stop eating

and become our rodeo hero again. The "squad" was still standing there, frozen. I guess they must have thought I had everything under control and was just exercising Siler or something!

He started running around wildly again, but then had a definite destination in mind. "He's heading for the highway! Stop him!" I shouted at the top of my lungs. Finally, this seemed to put the "firing squad" into action. The children started running, trying to block Siler from sprinting onto the highway. Uncle Jim handed me the rifle and took off trying to help. I wish there was some way to relate the fear, wildness and uncertainty of those minutes! He would race toward the highway, then suddenly charge one of the children. He was having a ball!

They finally got Siler to reverse his direction and he headed back to the ash pile. By now Susie and our smaller children were watching the action from the windows of the house. Siler snorted, turned around a few times and bucked his heels into the air. When he lowered his head to quickly grab some ashes, I took careful aim and shot him dead. As he fell to the ground, again, everyone just sort of stood there looking. "Where is the butcher knife? I need the butcher knife to slit his throat!" I shouted, my adrenalin at an all-time high. After a few disjointed grunts and half-sentences from the onlookers, a knife was finally handed to me.

Siler bled out like he was supposed to, but he was about 30 feet from the tree where we needed him. I ran to my tractor, but, as you can imagine, I couldn't get it started in that cold weather. Remember, its a *cute* tractor, not a *reliable* tractor. We hooked up a chain to Uncle Jim's van and dragged Siler closer to the tree.

The rest of the butchering of Siler went, well . . . fairly smoothly. Todd seemed to be impressed by the whole process (although he no longer believed the line: "It's a piece of cake. Nothing ever happens."). Since Jim and I were splitting the cow between us, we had to saw the carcass in half. It's a pretty long, hard process, cutting through the thick backbone. Toward the bottom, someone has to hold the giant pieces apart to keep the saw from getting stuck. Todd and I were both doing that while Jim finished up cutting. "I've almost got it," he said. The next thing I knew, Todd and I were lying on the ground, with half the beef on top of us, and heads that had a dull ache. Sort of stunned, too.

"Are you okay?" I asked Todd weakly, with visions of me standing in front of a judge trying to explain why Todd shouldn't sue me. It didn't help for Todd to jokingly say, "Where's my lawyer?" But after a few seconds, he laughed and said, "Yeah, I'm okay. But what happened?"

"At the split second that Jim finally made it through the last of the cut, the weight of the animal caused it to slide off the piece of wood it was hanging from," I said. I hoped Todd wasn't hurt and that he wouldn't have any hard feelings.

Todd had no hard feelings and even stuck around to help us cut up the meat into steaks and hamburger. Since it was getting late, we sat down to have some lunch. At one end of the table was a big set of ribs, with meat still hanging on it in places. I should note that it is a ten-foot long table, and we were eating on the clean end. Bloody knives were lying in a heap, and there was blood splattered on the table and floor. Yet the children ate their lunch like it was nothing. Todd was so amazed at the children being able to eat with a carcass on the table that he took a picture of the setting. He learned what we have learned. Our children are getting a more realistic perspective about life and death. They know that for something to live (like us) something has to die (like animals or plants).

My sixth cow to butcher was George. Remember George? He was Molly's calf, and was named after a veterinary missionary friend we have in Africa, George Mixon. I had only half steered him (it was back when I didn't know what I was doing) and he was getting pretty hard to get along with. He bullied the other cows and calves unmercifully, and with his long horns I was afraid he would do some real damage to them. He was always pawing the ground and sharpening his horns, which made a mess of the walls and fencing that he used as his "grinder." Of course, the final thing I didn't like about him was the fact that he was still part bull. His personality and blood line (remember Molly!) was not what I wanted in my stock.

At first, I thought I could just separate him from the other cows. To do this, I set up a pasture using an electric fence. This pasture was real close to my new garden spot, though I didn't think it would cause any problem. But it did. You see, he would come over to the edge of his pasture, right next to the electric fence, and just stare at the children about five feet away while they weeded the garden. Had that look in his eyes, kind of like Molly did. Even though there was an electric fence between George and the children, Susie and I didn't like the setup.

So I set up a new pasture a little further away from the one he was in and put him in there. I then gave the rest of the cows his "old" pasture because the main pasture wasn't doing too well from lack of rain. Well, the first day that I made all of these changes, George found some way to get out of his new pasture and join the other cows, including the heifers. That did it. It was time for George to go.

However, it was also the middle of June and we had been having record temperatures in the upper 90's (which was *very* unusual for up here!). You never want to butcher outside in warm weather because your meat can spoil. It's also no fun with millions of biting flies and mosquitoes filling the air. You really want to butcher when the ground is frozen, and, even better, if the ground is snow covered. But I was determined to have the problem of George behind me. So I set my alarm for 5:00 a.m. and went to bed. My decision rule was this: if it's not raining and it is 50 degrees F. or less, then I butcher him. The next morning at 5:00 a.m. it wasn't raining and the temperature was right at 50 degrees. Boy, I didn't want to do it, but there was no other way.

I grabbed my .22 magnum rifle with a scope and started my tractor. I had to make sure the tractor would actually start before I shot him. I could just see me shoot him, the tractor not start, and then I would get to watch him rot in the sunshine all that day.

I had an eerie feeling as I walked to George's pasture, with the tractor softly idling and the whole world apparently still asleep. Unlike every other time that I had walked by his pasture, this morning he refused to come up to the fence close to me. I had no choice but to go into his pasture and walk up to him. I was about four feet from him and we just sort of stared at each other. Raising my rifle, I looked through the scope but couldn't see George! It was too dark to make out much with that stupid scope on. I could have taken it off but that would have eaten up precious time, time that I didn't have with the soon-to-be-searing-sun already starting to rise.

I took the best shot I could and he dropped straight down. I ran forward and inserted our butcher knife to make the ear-to-ear cut. Nothing! The knife wouldn't cut. It seemed so dull I bet it wouldn't have cut warm butter. Now what to do? I ran to the house (about 600 feet away) and grabbed a few more knives. Arriving back at George, totally out of breath and panting hard (that's me, not George), I sliced away some more. None of those knives were worth a dime! Finally I was able to make an incision that started him bleeding well. But the cut was not as deep as I would have liked.

The sun was really rising quickly now. The 50° temperature seemed more like 80° to me. My family was still peacefully sleeping in their comfortable beds. I was sweating more and could feel my heart racing. Would I be able to get this silly bull completely skinned, gutted, and cut up before the heat and the flies descended in a very few hours? I didn't know that I could and also knew that I really didn't have any choice!

I tore back a big piece of the electric fence so I could drive in and hook up George and ran to the tractor. I gave it some gas and put it in gear. In my haste I must have let the clutch out too fast. It died. My thoughts were . . . well, they were full of worry. Carefully (my tractor requires tender loving care) I pushed on the starter. It started and I sighed with relief. It was a blessing from God.

After dragging George to the tree, I ran to get the ladder, come-along, chain, saws, and buckets. My skinning knife had the wrong blade in it so I had to run to the shop, find the right blade, and change it. Meanwhile, the clock ticked on. It was like all the nightmares I had while in graduate school. You must have had something like them, too. You know, where you have to be somewhere in five minutes, but you seem to be moving in super-slow motion while the hands on the clock on the wall are whizzing around and around, faster and faster. Then you finally reach that door you've been walking toward for so long, only to find it's the wrong one or is locked. It's the kind of nightmare I can do without!

Now that I was all set up, I skinned, gutted, and cut up the carcass into six pieces. I backed up the car and threw four of the pieces in the back (on a piece of plastic, obviously). I then took the other two pieces to the basement to cut up into hamburger. Having all of the meat tucked away, I cleaned up the area. I hooked up my little dump trailer to the riding lawn mower and loaded up all the guts, head, tail, hooves, etc. and carried them off to the woods. By 8:00, right about the time the flies started flying in earnest, I had everything cleaned up. Susie, sick from morning sickness, was so thankful that she didn't have to look at "the mess" and couldn't believe I got it all done before she got up.

I hurriedly ate some breakfast, then jumped in my van with Stevie to head to Bruce and Bekki Anderson's farm about an hour away. Bruce has a walk-in cooler and he said he would let my meat hang in his cooler for a few days. About a mile down the road Stevie suddenly said, "Hey Daddy, why is smoke coming into the car?" I looked over and didn't see any smoke and said that I thought it was just something coming out of the vents (I had the air conditioner on). But soon, I smelt and saw stuff spewing on the floorboard in front of his feet. I didn't know it at the time, but it was my heater core going out on me (a $300 repair, but that's another story). Turning around, we headed back home.

Most of my family was still in the driveway. Some of the children were still teary-eyed because they hadn't been allowed to go along with me. I usually take them just about everywhere, but this day I was too rushed to have to stop to let children go to the bathroom, etc. "Hey, Daddy's coming back!" someone yelled. I pulled the van into the garage and started silently transferring meat to my small Toyota. Since the Toyota wouldn't hold all the meat, I kept some in the back of the van and closed the garage doors, hoping to keep the meat somewhat cool while

I was gone. The temperature was climbing quickly. We were headed for another hot, muggy day in the mid 90's.

Stevie and I took off again, this time in a little more haste (if that is possible). I was afraid I was going to spoil all of my meat, and thus lose a lot of good food. God was very gracious to us and we were able to make it to Bruce's farm, hang the meat in his cooler, and return home and cut up the remaining meat for hamburger.

Sad to say but the meat grinder did not want to cooperate much that day, a fact that convinced me to purchase my own commercial-grade meat grinder. It would come in handy and certainly be of much use to my neighbors who also butcher their own beef. I attended a local farm auction a few weeks later and saw a very old meat grinder on one of the tables. Knowing who was selling it, I asked if it worked. "Oh, yeah, the motor works good," he said. I decided to bid on it. However, the auction dragged on and on, as auctions sometimes do. I decided that I was ready to leave and asked Dan Siler to bid on it for me. I gave him a maximum price to bid. After being home about 30 minutes, I wished I was back at the auction. Hopping into the car, I tried to get back before the grinder was put up. I was too late. It had sold to another man for a higher price than I had authorized Dan to bid. Disappointment sunk in deeply. Dan suggested that I try to buy it from the highest bidder. After some haggling, the highest bidder agreed to sell it to me for about $40 more than he had bid on it. How nice!

I took it home, cleaned it up, and installed some new parts. It didn't work! Stupid me. I took it to a repair shop to get an estimate on getting it fixed. While I was out, I stopped at Hobart and saw a reconditioned, guaranteed meat grinder for $1000. I bought it. A few weeks later, the repair shop called and said, "Your meat grinder is ready." "Ready? What do you mean ready?" I asked. "I only asked for an estimate!" Apparently the only real problem with the grinder is that I had plugged it into 110 volts instead of 220.

By the way, I ended up giving most of George's meat to a homeless shelter in the area. Since he was part bull, his meat tasted too gamey for us, especially Susie who was pregnant at the time.   The shelter gladly accepts all meat, even wild tasting venison, so the taste wasn't an issue for them.

I am not an expert butcher. I know I don't cut meat up the way anyone else in the world would do it.   I am sure that I probably turn some of the best cuts into hamburger by mistake. But I wouldn't trade the fact that I am butchering my own beef for all the money in the world. I know it is fresh, I know who handled it, I know that the utensils were clean and that there were no insects landing all over it, and I know how quickly it was put into the refrigerator or freezer.

Although it may sound like a lot of work, butchering beef really is not all that hard.   In fact, I am always surprised and amazed at the amount of meat you get for the amount of effort that you put into butchering.   It usually takes me about 8-10 hours from the time I lead the animal out of the barn until I place the last package of beef in the freezer.   And raising and butchering my own beef saves me a lot of money.   Including all cuts (steak, roast, hamburger, stew, etc.) Todd-the-cow ended up costing me $0.62 per pound, Star cost $0.48 per pound, and George cost me basically nothing.   That is hard to beat!

It's also nice to know that our beef animals are treated kindly.   They don't spend their lives sloshing through a pit of manure.   They don't have to worry about overcrowding or being able to get their fair share of food and water.   Instead, they live in sunshine, and get plenty of fresh grass and good hay.   They have a nice clean loafing shed to get out of the heat and find some relief from biting flies.   Their water is always fresh and clean. We're happy about our setup.   Raising beef is definitely something we'll continue to do.

Chapter 10
Did You Say Sheep?

Men, when you are trying to think of a nice, thoughtful gift for your wife, what kinds of things do you consider? If you are like me, you want to get her something that she will enjoy, that she won't be able to guess, that she doesn't already have, and that won't bankrupt you! Also, if you're like me, that's a hard thing to come up with.

Well, for Susie's last birthday, I thought I had hit the jackpot. You see, she's really into doing things the old-fashioned way. She likes to make soap, bake bread, sew her own clothes, and cook on her small Monarch woodburning stove. She prefers hardwood floors and dress patterns that would fit right in during the 1800's. Anyway, I knew that she had always talked about spinning wool, so what better gift to get her than a spinning wheel?

Now that's not an item that WalMart keeps in stock. In fact, most things that Susie likes are not stocked at WalMart. In fact, most things that Susie likes aren't stocked anywhere anymore! When was the last time you came across a horse-drawn buggy or a sheet of 1920's style original linoleum at a yard sale you visited? When was the last time you saw a hand-operated wringer for washing clothes or an old fashioned wooden butter churn that worked great? Chances are if you did find something like that, you were either looking at one that was pretty dilapidated (which would only have value to a collector) or you were at a very specialized dealer that catered to those "weird" kinds of things. It was just such a dealer that I had to contact to get a spinning wheel.

Actually, "spinning" is not so out of vogue. There are many women (and I suppose men, too) who have taken up this craft in the last fifteen years or so. There are spinning guilds in most cities as well as a number of festivals and gatherings all across the country specifically for spinners. Spinning conferences, exhibits, shows, schools, special sales, handbooks, and a bunch of magazines (like *Spin Off, Black Sheep Newsletter, The Spinning Wheel Sleuth*, etc.) further illustrate the interest in spinning. Most spinners today do so only occasionally, for a hobby or relaxation or to make a very special small item for a close friend. I believe Susie, on the other hand, had visions of spinning all of her own threads and then turning them into fabric with which to make clothing. That's what they used to do 100 years ago, so don't laugh. It's not so outlandish.

Since I didn't see "Spinning Wheels" in the Yellow Pages (I tried to let my fingers do the walking) I decided to call one of Susie's friends, Laura LaValley, who is a spinner. Laura was planning to teach Susie how to spin on her wheel, so I thought it would be good to buy a wheel like Laura's. Laura told me of several places to buy wheels, and gave me information about the various brands to choose from. I made a few calls, and decided I liked the Ashford wheel. Ashford was the brand of wheel that Laura had and it was a good "starter" wheel. That should have caused a light to go off in my head. If they have starter wheels, you must need to upgrade at some time to an intermediate wheel, and then to an expert wheel. I also liked the Ashford brand because it was a lot cheaper (I'm sorry, I mean "less expensive") than the other ones I looked at.

Anyway, I called an Ashford wheel dealer about 1 ½ hours away and said, "I need a spinning wheel." She proceeded to ask me a ton of questions, like: "What will she be spinning on it? What kind of wool? How about cotton, Angora rabbit hair or goat hair; will she be spinning any of those also? How often do you think she will be spinning? Do you want a traditional model, a traveler model (that is easy to carry if you want to spin in lots of locations) or did you want an old-fashioned "big" wheel? Did you want an electric wheel or one that is hand-operated?" To each question, I just answered, "I don't know. I just need a spinning wheel."

She shipped me a traditional Ashford wheel by UPS along with a bill for $212. It arrived in a small plain brown box (in case

Susie was around when it arrived). As I looked at the size of the thin box, I remembered the dealer saying that I would need to assemble it. As I uncrated it, I also remembered that I was going to get to "finish" it (with paint, stain, etc.). Neither of these would be any problem, except that I didn't want Susie to see it. Also, my work shop was pretty cold (it was winter already). It's not generally recommended to stain or polyurathene something with the temperature at 10°F. Thankfully, I had recently installed a small woodburning heater in the shop. My biggest fear was that it would get too cold in there at night when I couldn't (or wouldn't) get up and stoke the fire, keeping the shop warm. It was my only choice, though, so I busted open the box.

Putting together some things is not all that difficult. Just take a bicycle, for example. You pick up the two wheels out of the box and instantly you know where they are supposed to be installed. You look at the handlebars and you don't even think of putting them on the end of the pedal. I'm not saying it is real easy to put together a bike (the assembly manual for my Huffy bike was 26 pages long), but at least you know something about what you are installing. Not so for me with a spinning wheel. I had never heard of a maiden bar, flyer whorl, adjusting board, or drive band tension spring. I couldn't even remember how you use a spinning wheel, although I had casually watched people do it at historic reenactments and craft shows. Ashford enclosed a four-page assembly guide, complete with lots of pictures. For that I was thankful. But in just reading the directions I never figured out if my wheel was a single drive or double drive system, and thus, didn't know which set of instructions to follow at times. As I studied the instruction manual, I also gave some thought as to what color the wheel should be stained.

Since this was going to be a piece to be displayed in the living room, what stain would look best? We have a hodgepodge of woods and stains in that room, and I didn't know whether to make it cherry (like the rocking chair, quilt rack, and grandfather clock), black walnut (like the barrister bookcases, end tables, and hope chest), or oak (like the hutch/secretary and flooring). I sure didn't want to get it all done and have Susie say, "Oh, thanks!

It's great! It couldn't be better. That is, unless it was oak." Susie is easy to please, so I didn't really expect that conversation. But she does have some definite ideas about what she likes.

I asked the children what color I should stain it. I got some helpful suggestions, but it didn't relieve my fear that I might do the wrong thing. Finally, I decided to spoil Susie's birthday by telling her ahead of time what she was getting (so she could choose the color). As you guessed it, she was ecstatic to be getting a spinning wheel. As for color, "Oh, it doesn't really matter to me. Black walnut would be okay, but it really doesn't matter," she said. While I was glad she was open to colors, it did make me wish I hadn't spoiled her surprise. As to color, black walnut it was going to be!

I finally figured out how to connect the maiden bar to the adjusting board; just where to put the flyer hooks, brake band tension knob, and drive belt adjusting knob; and got the whole spinning wheel assembled. I also assembled the Lazy Kate, a little $15 contraption whose only job is to hold three little spools of spun wool. Apparently, when you have three spools full, you "run" the content of these spools back through the wheel, forming a thicker, single spool of wool with which to knit.

So, we were set. Right? Wrong. You can't just pick up a sheep's fleece and start spinning it. First it has to be washed and combed (called "carding"). Washing involves removing any hay or junk found in the fleece and rinsing away the dirt. But combing requires the purchase/finishing/assembly of another item: hand cards. When I learned that I definitely needed to buy hand cards, I called my dealer back and she shipped the $42 set of cards out right away. Spinning wool, I was learning, can be an expensive proposition.

The day finally arrived and Susie "officially" got her birthday presents. Laura LaValley came over and taught Susie how to spin on Susie's new wheel. There was a bunch of excitement that day! They washed, carded, and spun a piece of fleece that Laura had. The only problem they had was that the wheel seemed to be going too fast! Uh-oh, had I assembled it wrong? Had I placed the maiden bar on upside down? No matter how much we fiddled with it we couldn't get it to spin slowly. Later, we learned that we should adjust the speed by turning the brake band tension knob. Now why didn't I think of that earlier?

Susie and the girls got pretty good at spinning the wool. So much so that we had to buy another fleece to practice on for $45. They also kept talking about needing a Niddy Noddy (cost of about $20), which is a little contraption that makes it easy to skein the wool. But Stevie and I made our own version of a Niddy Noddy, by looking at Laura's.

Since they had all the equipment, and had gotten pretty good at spinning wool, the thought entered Susie's head, "Hey, why not buy some sheep? After all, we have a farm. That way, we wouldn't have to buy fleeces from other people. And I'll bet we could sell any of our excess fleeces to other hand spinners in the area." So she started making phone calls. Long distance phone calls. Long (in terms of time) long distance phone calls! Seems it all paid off though, because she had located several Border Leicester sheep only an hour away. But it was important that we go pick them up right away. The sheep were pregnant and due to lamb in eight weeks. The owner said they could only travel safely for about two more weeks. We thought about going and getting them, but the weather was getting very cold. Then as Susie was talking to another lady, she learned that the Border Leicester breed of sheep is indeed good for hand spinning, but only if you are going to use them to weave rugs. The Border Leicester's fleece is coarse, though it wears well.

What we really needed, Susie learned, was Corriedale sheep. She located a farm of Corriedale sheep that was selling out. These ladies also had Angora goats. One of the ladies had lots of trouble with her knees, including surgery, so she felt sheep were getting too hard for her to handle. By the time Susie got in touch with the owners, they had already sold over half their flock, and someone had offered to buy any that remained. If Susie wanted the pick of their flock, she had to get there first!

On a very, very cold morning Susie, Jeannie, Stevie, and Elijah hopped in the van and headed to pick up the ewes (female sheep). I was staying at home with the rest of the children because that was the morning we were going to butcher Siler, a story I related in the last chapter. Susie looked them over and relied heavily on the advice of the owners for picking out some good ones for hand spinning. She crammed five fat ewes in the back of the van and started home. "My only regret is that I couldn't fit any more in," was her comment to me later.

On the way home, the ewes and the people in the car must have done a good bit of exhaling, because the windows repeatedly fogged, and froze. Within 30 minutes, a sheet of hard ice had formed over the inside of the windows, and the only way to keep the windshield clear enough to see was to keep the windows rolled down. Remember that, with the wind chill, it was about 20° below zero. Since the car was traveling at about 40 MPH, that could bring the wind chill in the car down to around -80° (but only where the wind was actually coming in the car--besides, the car's heater was going full blast). Baby Elijah was in his snow suit, but Susie was afraid that he would get frost bite. So every so often she would close the windows for a while, until things started getting iced over again. The children were also helping by scraping the windows, from the inside, so they could see out. Because the roads were not in great shape, the driving part of the trip alone was four hours round trip! By the time they got home, Susie and the children were exhausted. The rest of us who had stayed home were also exhausted, after butchering and cutting up the steer!

We put the sheep in an enlarged 13' x 36' area I had made for them in the barn. There was no way to keep their water from freezing, so we installed a $34 bucket water heater. With $30 of minerals, oats, and corn, we were in good shape.

The ewes we had bought were not bred back. That was odd, since it was the first of February. Usually, the sheep are bred back in the fall, with resulting spring lambs. Susie got to thinking more about lambs, and how those ewes were not bred back, and decided that a ram was called for. We thought about renting a ram, but decided to see if we could buy one instead. More long distance calls. We finally found a ram that we could get for only $60.

This time it was my turn to pick up a smelly animal in the van (I volunteered). So, Stevie, Jeannie and I loaded up in the van and headed to the "iron range" of Minnesota. The roads were in pretty bad condition, with only two lanes of the four lane highway in a somewhat safe condition. And it was cold! My windshield washer stopped working, but that didn't keep other cars' slush from messing up my windshield. I stopped at a convenience store, bought a gallon of windshield washer, and sloshed some onto the windshield periodically. The trip was not starting out well.

Two hours later, we finally approached the vicinity of the farm with the ram. The more we got off the main road, the worse the road conditions became. I was beginning to wonder if we should just turn around and head back home, when we finally reached the driveway of the ram's owner.

A big woolly, loud sheep dog came bounding out to the car to greet me. Would the dog bite? I didn't know and didn't want to get out of the car to find out. What are your options in those situations? You can sit in the car and hope that someone will look out the window and come to your rescue. We tried that. It didn't work. Or, you can sit in your car and blow your horn. We tried that. It didn't work. Or, you can drive away. After two hours of cleaning my windshield by hand on a freezing cold day I didn't like that option either. Or, of course you can get out of your car and start banging on the door. That's what I finally did. I can't remember why they said they didn't notice the dog barking its head off or the horn beeping, but we walked out to the ram pen.

This ram was supposed to be gentle and afraid of people, which was the main reason we wanted to buy him. Rams don't generally have the best reputation on a farm for kindness to people. The owner, a small fragile-looking man, walked into the ram pen to get Bo, our ram. There were about 8-10 rams in that pen, and some of them were pretty big! This frail man didn't seem a bit afraid, though, and kept trying to persuade Bo to come out of a little shed he was hiding in. Finally, the man said he would just go in there and bring Bo out. That took courage because there were a number of rams "holed up" in there.

After he went in, three or four big rams came charging out of the building and then finally the man came out holding Bo's head. To handle a ram safely you hold his head up. That way, he can't butt you, which is about the only thing he can do in the way of harmful things. We finally got the ram loaded into the van, said "thanks" and started the long voyage back to the house. I was thankful, again, for that unwritten rule that says it is the seller's job to load your purchased animals!

If anything the road conditions had gotten worse. Now the single lane on my side of the road that was "good" was not that great. There was a lot of slow-moving traffic, and no way to pass anyone. I got behind a log truck that was flinging snow, ice, slush, and road salt all over my car. Remember that my windshield washer didn't work. I was having fun.

Then we started to smell it. It was not much at first, but it got stronger. "What's that smell?" asked the children. The smell got worse. I decided to open my windows. And it was really cold! So with the heat on high, the windows all rolled down, and me sloshing cleaner on the windshield, we rolled down the highway. For some reason people kept staring at us. When they saw the ram, people would go so far as to point at us. Oh well, only a few more hours till we will be home again.

I had the radio on, probably pretty loud too, in order to hear it over the noise of the wind blowing into the car. Suddenly, both Stevie and Jeannie in unison shouted, "CHANGE THE RADIO! OW!!!" I about wrecked the car trying to figure out what the problem was. Was the radio somehow shocking them in the back seat? Had they finally lost their mind due to the numbing cold and blaring radio? Did they want me just to change the radio station? When I settled down a little bit and asked them to explain their outburst, they laughingly replied that they had just read the message on an outdoor billboard. Apparently, the billboard at one time had read: Change your radio . . . NOW! , but had lost the letter "N." The children thought it was all funny, but I was secretly trying to measure my pulse and blood pressure.

Buying that innocent sounding spinning wheel which resulted in owning sheep was turning out to be a lot of fun.

When we finally did get home (yes, things like that trip do come to an end eventually), we backed the van up to the barn door. I wasn't sure where the ram would go and didn't want him getting lost in the snow drifts. I thought about tying him up to a long rope, but remembering my experience with Molly, the cow, I decided not to. I thought I would just "drag" him back to the sheep pen by holding his head up, like that little man, his former owner, had done. Only it wasn't as easy as it had looked. Besides, after a few steps inside the barn, Bo smelt the ewes and ran as fast as he could for their pen! It didn't take any coaxing!

It was okay to have the sheep in the barn, but we wanted them out in the pasture too. Only problem is that the mineral block that we buy for the cows will kill the sheep if they eat too much of it (apparently sheep can't handle all the copper that cows can). A solution was to buy a mineral block that would be safe for both cows and sheep, although it was more expensive ($9) than a regular mineral block ($4.45). I put the expensive mineral block out and let the sheep out into the pasture with our cows. Those silly cows acted like I had dropped a big piece of candy on the ground. They fought each other for the rights to eat huge hunks of that mineral block! They would eat it so fast and hard that it would get shoved under the fence. When it was retrieved and placed back in the pasture, the cows would attack it again! They ended up eating that one block in three days (a regular mineral block usually lasts 3-4 months on our farm). Let's see, at $9 every three days, the minerals alone for the sheep would cost me $1095 per year!

Thus, it was decided to separate the sheep and the cows using electric fencing. It was impossible to drive fence posts in the frozen ground up here until around the first of May, so the sheep had to make do with their pen in the barn until then. When we did separate them, it worked well. Later I learned that it wasn't necessary to separate them much, because the sheep didn't seem interested in the cow's mineral block at all. We put up an electric fence near the barn doors because we wanted the sheep to be able to get into the barn, but not the cows. We raised it high enough that the sheep could go under it to get to the pasture. The cows couldn't stoop down, though, and get into the barn. The system worked well.

In late spring, we had a shearer come in and shear the sheep for $25. Now it was time to sell the fleeces. I was excited about the chance to get a return on all of my investments of time and money. But almost all the people who said they would love to buy our sheeps' fleeces, decided that they didn't really need any after all. We did sell one complete fleece and about 3 pounds of other ones. But still our gross income from the fleeces was only $40, not a lot of money.

Also, we needed the hay that they were eating for our growing herd of beef cows. We didn't want to end up buying hay. The beef cows were useful to us--we do eat beef. Even though many people eat sheep, we don't care to.

We thought of selling the sheep. The first few people that we thought might be interested turned out not to be. Then we located a man who said he would be willing to buy our sheep if they were healthy. Only he said that ewes which are not bred back are only worth about $30 in the summer.

On top of that, Susie and the girls weren't spinning any-more. They still did it, on very rare occasions, but they were all too busy to just leisurely sit down and spin. We had boxes of fleeces in the basement waiting for someone to start spinning. Every time I would see a moth in the house I was worried that it was getting its supper at our expense (by eating the wool in the basement!).

But what about those baby lambs? We didn't get any. I guess Bo was not successful in "breeding back" the ewes in the winter. It was a long shot, actually, and we knew it. Fall is the usual time that ewes are bred back.

Finally, we faced the facts. Fact 1: The sheep require hay, water, pasture and care. Fact 2: No one was knocking down our door to buy our fleeces. Fact 3: We weren't even spinning the fleeces we had. Fact 4: Let's say we had lambs. What would we do with them, honestly? Raise them to have *more* fleeces? Sell the cute, cuddly little things to be butchered? And how would we keep them penned up and off the highway? Fact 5: Others in the area who said they had tried sheep or had seriously considered it, felt that sheep would never "make money." Considering all those facts, we decided to try and sell them again. This time, we called a friend, who called several friends. Yes, one was interested. We finally sold the sheep for $40 each, giving us a net loss on the sheep of $288.33. Not good. But not horrible either. I believe I can safely state that we have "closed the chapter" on owning sheep.

Chapter 11
Fixing Up the Farmhouse

There I stand, precariously balanced on an icy roof, reaching above my head to the next layer of bricks. It's ten degrees F and the brick that was wet just a few seconds ago is now well frozen to my gloved hand. The wind is starting to blow again. Having already witnessed bricks, tools, and a piece of scaffolding slide off the slick roof, I wonder, "Will something else be blown off? Will it be me that will be blown off with the next gust of icy wind?" That wouldn't be good since no one is outside making sure that I am all right by watching me. It's just too cold to be outside more than a few minutes.

Just a few hours ago I needed help, and listening down the chimney, could hear the sound of people laughing and talking in the kitchen. I shouted, "Hey! Somebody! Hey!" down the chimney till I was hoarse, but no one heard me. And the thick blanket of snow we will almost certainly have in a few months, which would provide some cushion to my fall, is not here yet. All that is down there is frozen ground and about ½ inch of snow and ice.

What if the chimney I am building collapses on top of me, pinning me beneath its oppressive weight? How long before someone would find me up here on the roof? And how am I going to get through with these next four rows of bricks, get my tools and myself cleaned up, drive 35 minutes to the university, and be there for the 3:30 P.M. meeting when it is already 2:30 P.M.? On top of all that, it looks like I may run out of cement before I get the last few bricks laid. That means I'll either have to run to the basement and mix up another batch, or just put off finishing this project for a few days because they are forecasting a snow storm later tonight. This is not the first job I've tackled on the farmhouse, and somehow I'll get through this mess. I'll relate the rest of this particular episode later in this chapter, after I have told you of some of those other experiences.

Fixing up and maintaining a farmhouse often sounds romantic, and to some of you, may create an image more like the following:

> A man, whistling in the soft morning sunlight as the birds whistle back to him, walks from his workshop with a piece of wood he has carefully crafted to fix a small problem in his home. A child runs up to him, and he scoops the child up in his arms, laughing as he continues to walk toward the house. Inside, the man hammers on the new piece of wood as the child watches breathlessly. It fits perfectly; no need for any more trips to the shop with this project. Everyone applauds his ingenuity and skill. Since he doesn't have any-thing else to do, he suggests homemade ice cream and a walk in the woods.

Sounds appealing, doesn't it? Romantic too. And things do turn out like that sometimes as you fix up your farm buildings. But they can often turn out just like the narrative at the beginning of this chapter. I would like to share with you some examples of both, experiences that have resulted in our farm (and myself) taking on a different look than when we moved in.

As I related in an earlier chapter, we had to have major remodeling work done just to be able to squeeze our family into this little bungalow. I won't comment on that except to say that my contract purposefully did not include many things that most remodeling agreements would include (like flooring, cabinets, painting, counter tops, etc.). I felt that I could do a lot of the work, over a several-year time period, and thus save some money.

Painting

One of the main items on the agenda was to get every square inch of the inside of the house cleaned and painted. Ben was allergic to dog hair (the previous owners had inside dogs) and we felt that painting would remove any final traces of that offensive substance. I made many, many trips to WalMart, buying interior primer and wall paint. I also had to learn how to patch plaster walls, because we had some water damage in the upstairs rooms.

Painting and plaster repair is not a particularly difficult job, it is just a tedious one. You feel like you're never going to get finished. The sequence is the following: Clean the walls. Patch holes and cracks in the walls. Clean and put away your tools. Cover the floor. Prime the walls. Clean your tools (and the floor; the cheap plastic drop cloths never stay put!). Paint the walls. Clean your tools again (and the floor; there is another thing about those little plastic drop cloths. If you spill paint on them, and then walk on them, you will spread that paint with your shoes). Put a second coat of paint on the walls. Clean your tools (and the floor again!). Clean, patch, caulk, prime, paint, and then repaint the windows and trim. All finished? Now it's time to move to the next room and start all over again. Before a few rooms are complete, you start to ask yourself the age-old question: "I wonder what it would cost to have someone come in and do this for me?"

Which reminds me of something one of our contractors once said when discussing remodeling and painting the house. He simply stated, "I never did learn how to paint." How convenient! Pretty smart, too! Sometime some of you may wish you would have heard that excuse, and adopted it for yourself, before ever picking up that very first paint brush many years ago.

We also had to scrape, caulk, prime, paint, and repaint all of the outside of the house. This was harder because it was in terrible shape. The paint was peeling off all over the place. It was also made harder by the fact that I had to do a lot of the work while standing on ladders, or, for the dormers, on top of the house. I'm not really fond of heights. About the only thing I would mention about painting the outside of the house is that it took me a lot longer than I ever dreamed it could. If you're like me, you should estimate the time it will take you to do a job and then at least double it!

It's important to use the right tools. On one of my former

homes I used a regular paint brush for very coarse siding. It took me forever to paint it! I must have learned a lesson because in this farmhouse I painted the textured ceiling with a special roller made just for textured surfaces. Special tools don't usually cost much more (if any) than normal tools. Get the right tool for the job!

Installing hardwood floors

After the contractors were through and totally out of the house, it was possible to install the flooring. The easiest flooring is probably carpet.   The best thing about carpeting is that someone comes in and installs it for you. You don't have any work to do except moving the wrists while writing the check. But that wasn't an option for us for several reasons. First, Ben had some pretty bad allergies, something for which carpeting is not good. Carpets are full of noxious chemicals that can trigger an allergic reaction. We saw this first hand, as we visited home improvement centers that also sold carpet. Very soon we had family members sneezing and coughing. Second, we just didn't want carpet. We liked the look and "feel" of having hardwood floors.

Have you priced hardwood floors lately? If not, get ready for some "sticker shock!" If you just walk into a flooring retailer, pick out nice hardwood, and have it installed, you'll probably pass out when the bill is handed to you. We didn't really want to pass out, so we started looking for a "deal." And we found one.

About 1 ½ hours south of us, a hardwood floor sawmill, Tex's Lumber, sold directly to the public. Not like they had big signs announcing the fact, though. When we first went to look at flooring, we couldn't even find the place. We had to call several times to get directions and redirections until we finally stumbled on it out in a rural area. At Tex's, you are buying directly at the mill where the big oak logs are cut, planed, and kiln-dried into finished flooring.   In fact, when you drive back to load the flooring up in your car, you drive by huge stacks of enormous oak logs, awaiting their destiny of being cut into flooring. The prices we got were even cheaper than buying a good carpet and having it installed.

Rather than trying to lay all of the floors at one time, we did it in three groups: the kitchen (12' x 24'), the living room "addition" (12' x 24'), and the upstairs bedrooms (two rooms at 12' x 12' each). By breaking it up, I was able to do the job without breaking my back. Laying flooring is not hard. First, we swept the floor clean and cut away some of the subflooring of the original house. This was necessary in order to have a completely flat area to work on. In some places the subflooring of the original house was about ½ inch higher than the subflooring of the new addition. Cutting away that ½ inch ended up being quite a job! I used an electric hand-held planer to get most of it off, but still had to rely on chisels to do a lot. I learned the value of using really sharp chisels!

After getting the subflooring uniformly level, I stapled down a thin, red roll of paper that the supply house called "Red X" paper. Its purpose is to prevent squeaking of the flooring, which is accomplished by keeping the subfloor and hardwood floor from rubbing together, I guess. I take it most people just use tar paper to do this, but we didn't want to because we were afraid that Ben might have a reaction to the chemicals in the tar paper.

Now that the paper was stapled down, we marked a starting point and snapped a chalk line. We found this starting point by deciding which wall we were going to call straight, and then measured 3 7/8 inches from that wall. Our flooring was 3 1/8 inches in width and we wanted a 3/4 inch gap between the flooring and the wall. With a good clean line to work from, Jeff Berthiaume and I then power-nailed the first row of flooring so that it came right up to the line. Remember Jeff? He's our neighbor, and a master carpenter by trade. He also has the best selection of quality tools anyone could hope to borrow!

Putting down flooring was actually fun and easy. It amazed me that Jeff's air tool could drive a nail straight through tough 3/4 inch oak flooring, but it was set at 120 psi, which is a lot of pressure! It was important to nail the starter course (the first row) down very securely, because all of the rest of the flooring would be slammed into it to get the floor good and tight. In fact, Jeff suggested that we nail the first two rows of flooring down to make a super strong "backstop" for all the slamming that was going to occur.

With my starter rows firmly in position, I started installing the rest of the flooring. To do this I rented a hand-operated nailing tool from a local rental place. It cost me $40 rental a day and they also sold the nails that were used in the tool. Basically, you put the board down where you want it and tap it into position as tightly as you can. Then you pick up this tool, which holds a row of nails inside itself, and place its base over the lip of your tongue and grooved flooring. The tool is designed to fit into the grooves perfectly. With a single strong slam of a rubber hammer you hit the plunger of the tool, which tightens the flooring even more closely together and drives a long nail deep into the subflooring. You then move the tool down the plank some and slam it again. You want to drive a nail into each floor joist and one in between as well. It's amazing how well this little nonelectric, nonhydraulic hand-operated tool works! The flooring is jammed together very tightly and makes it look like a professional has installed it. All it requires is strength and stamina. After a few hours, your arms get tired of slamming it. My children, who begged me to let them try, found out that they were not strong enough to drive a nail totally in.

It is important, when installing hardwood floors, to leave a gap on all sides so the wood can expand and contract. I suppose if you didn't it would just warp or buckle. We kept a 3/4 inch crack on all sides of our flooring to prevent this from happening. The baseboard and quarter round finishing pieces we installed covered up that crack around the walls with no problem. The only problem we had was where the new floor met the existing hardwood floor, always in the middle of the room. In every case the new floor met the old floor at a 90-degree angle (meaning that the boards of the two floors were perpendicular, not parallel to each other). We felt we had to maintain a 3/4 inch space and yet we had to connect the two rooms somehow. Our solution was to leave the 3/4 inch gap but then cover that gap with a strip of 3/8 inch thick oak about 2 inches wide. I nailed this cover strip of oak into the middle of the gap, thus not binding either floor to the cover strip. In theory, both floors can expand and contract as the weather changes but the cover strip will stay where it is. And it has worked beautifully!

The only problem is that we now have what look like small "speed bumps" at four places in our house. Like I said, they are only about 3/8 inch thick and don't cause us much trouble. It's not like you are going to trip over them. If you are sweeping that room, you just make two piles, one on each side of the bump. No big deal. The only ones who have a problem with them are the little bitty children. Elijah was learning to walk by pushing a five-gallon can filled with flour (with the lid on, usually!) across the floors. No problem, until he hit one of those "speed bumps." Then he would usually cry until someone came and "got him over the hump." As he got a little older and smarter, however, he would have five gallon buckets (some filled with flour, some with wheat kernels, some with milk powder, etc.) placed strategically on all sides of those "speed bumps." Then, when he wanted to move from room to room, he would scoot his bucket along until it hit a "speed bump," transfer to a waiting bucket on the other side of the bump, and continue his journey. It reminded me of how Tarzan used those rope swings to move from tree to tree. As Tarzan would near the outer "swing" of his rope, there would always be another one hanging there for him to catch, and thus he could keep swinging through the jungle. Well, Elijah did the same thing, except with five gallon buckets.

The only other thing you have to do to install the hardwood flooring is to cut the planks so they fit the contours and corners of your room. For this, again, I borrowed from Jeff. His electric cutoff saw (or chop saw, some people call it) was invaluable. I was able to make perfectly straight 90 degree cuts exactly where I needed them. Thanks again, Jeff!

The floor was installed. I filled knot holes and cracks with wood putty and hand sanded any little places that needed some touch up. Most people would bring in a big electric floor sander and get the floor totally level and sanded down. I didn't do this for two reasons. First, the floor was almost perfectly level as it was. Second, I didn't want to create all of the dust that a big sander makes. It will about drive you out of the house and the dust gets everywhere. Not a good situation for a little guy with asthma. Most people have commented that the floors look great without being sanded anyway.

To finish the flooring, we didn't use the usual polyurethane. Again, we didn't want the chemicals in the house. Also, we knew from experience that polyurethane, after a few years, can start to peel off and flake. Once that happens your only solution is to sand the floors again and put down a fresh coat of polyurethane. Instead, we put down two coats of tung oil, a natural product. This seals and protects the floor. This we followed with two coats of household floor wax. We were done! In terms of maintenance we wax the kitchen and dining room floor several times a year because of its unusual wear and tear. The rest of the rooms haven't needed any care at all since we installed them over three years ago. We can add more tung oil if we want at any time (after the wax is removed) without having to sand the floors. We're very pleased with the results of our hardwood floor installation!

Building kitchen cabinets and a pantry

It would have been easy to run to the building supply house and order a complete set of kitchen cabinets. In fact, in the other houses we have built I have always had them custom-built for me. But we were into self-sufficiency and it didn't seem like it would be too hard to build them. Especially since Susie wanted very PLAIN white cabinets, with no raised panels or glass included. You know, just plain flat cabinets.

I studied plans for cabinets in books I could find. I collected information about standard heights, depths, and spaces needed for standard appliances. Then I went to the building supply store and bought a good grade of sanded birch plywood, some 1 x 2's, some 2 x 4's, and headed to my shop. Later, I would get my shop in good shape with everything straightened up and all tools in their proper place. During the time I was building those cabinets, I was still storing tons of stuff in the shop, and all of my tools were not accessible. I felt cramped.

I also felt like I just wanted to get this job over with. That's too bad. It is important in life to learn to enjoy the process, not just the finished product. That is a hard lesson for someone like me to learn. I need to slow down more. I need to stop and reflect, on occasion, on what I have done to that point. Most things in life are not two steps: 1) decide to do something and 2) you're done. There are lots of "things" that occur between those two steps. In fact, MOST of life consists of "things" that occur between those two steps! For your own happiness in life, you had better learn to enjoy those "things".

I'm afraid I didn't always enjoy the process when building the kitchen cabinets. But they did get built. I then primed and painted them with white enamel, just as Susie wanted. They looked fine.

For a counter top, most people will just go and buy one or have one built. You know, that modern kind that has the big back lip (splash guard) built right in. That's not the old-fashioned look, however, and Susie wanted an old-fashioned look. She didn't want that built-in back lip. I was able to buy the plastic 1/16 inch thick counter top material in a 12-foot piece and then glue it to the flat piece of plywood I had nailed to the top of the base cabinets. Then I installed a chrome front lip and chrome back lip (very old-fashioned looking!) that we bought from Berger Hardware, a local old-fashioned hardware store that still sells many neat old things. With that the kitchen cabinets were finished.

Building the pantry was easy. In one corner of the kitchen, I just built sort of a box by nailing 2 x 4's from floor to ceiling. Then, I closed the "box" in with plywood on the side. I built a cabinet-style face on the front (using 1 x 4's) , added huge doors and shelves, primed, painted, and I was done. The only problem I had was that the floor was not exactly parallel with the ceiling. I corrected for that by having the face overlap the outside a little bit at the top. Thus, when one looks at the pantry from the front it looks, and is, perfectly straight up and down.

Remodeling bathrooms

Our two existing bathrooms worked, but we felt they could use some sprucing up. For the main floor bathroom, sprucing up consisted of a new toilet, new sink, new medicine cabinet, new flooring, new light fixtures, some changes in the electrical wiring, and a new wall covering. Other than that we didn't do much in that room, meaning that the tub was the only thing we didn't change!

First, I tore out the old medicine cabinet because it had not been installed flush with the wall (there was a vent pipe that prevented this). It stuck out into the room too far, exposing some wiring (that wasn't even hooked up) and basically didn't achieve the look we wanted. Where the cabinet had been, I had a big hole which had to be patched with a new piece of sheetrock. With sheetrock comes taping and puttying, over and over. I found a kind of tape that is already sticky, making it easier to apply. Without that stickiness, the tape always falls off the wall before I can get the putty to hold it up there. I am thankful for many of the modern inventions we have today, like sticky sheetrock tape.

I then removed the existing sink and toilet. That seemed like a pretty big deal to me. It wasn't hard at all, but I sure felt "under the gun" to get the new stuff installed soon. Even though we had two other bathrooms in the house (one in the basement and a brand new one from our new construction upstairs), it is nice and convenient to have one on the main floor of your house. I crammed a rag in the drain for the toilet to keep the sewer gases from entering the house. My fear was that someone (perhaps a child?) would walk in and quietly stuff the rag on down into the 4" drain pipe. But it didn't happen. Why do we "borrow trouble" by thinking of all of the things that could go wrong instead of focusing on all of the things that have gone right? It's something to think about.

After I installed the new light fixtures and painted the room, it was time to install a new wall covering. We had chosen to install 3 inch wide strips of tongue-and-groove pine paneling that was to be about four feet high. Again, this went well with the help of Jeff's air compressor and nail gun. It looked so good in its natural finish that we decided not to stain it any other color. We applied several coats of satin finish polyurethane. Oh, and we also painted the back of the boards with polyurethane before we installed them, because Robin said it would help to keep them from warping and mildewing so badly. And he was right, as usual.

When I was preparing to return the tools to Jeff's house, Stevie asked if he could come along and help. He hopped out to open our gate, and I drove through. After he shut the gate, Stevie headed to the car and I shouted to him, "Remember, don't step on Mr. Berthiaume's tools!" Stevie misunderstood me and thought I said, "Remember to step on Mr. Berthiaume's tools!" So he did. He jumped in the van's back door, stepped on the little air gun, then the big air gun, then the nails, then he climbed onto the air compressor, and then jumped over the back seat. He was very thorough in following what he thought I had told him to do! Sorry, Jeff.

Actually, there are lots of times when children don't listen well or quite fully understand what is being communicated. When we went to Canada, the customs officer asked me a lot of questions, like, "Do you have any guns, knives, . . . illegal drugs? Are all of these children yours? How long will you stay in Canada? What are you going to do in Canada? etc." All of this was ended with the phrase, "Have a good day!" A few weeks after we got home, the little children were pretending to be Canadian customs officers. I stopped long enough to hear Betsy ask Ben: "Do you have any guns, or knives?. . . Oh, you don't? Well, here's some (said while pretending to hand Ben some knives)! Have a good day!"

I learned that it is possible for a do-it-yourself-er to install new plumbing and eventually get it all to stop leaking. They make so many products now to make it much easier. Like flexible supply lines (those are the "hoses" that connect from your water lines to your sink or toilet). In the old days, you had to cut and bend the supply lines perfectly to fit between the incoming water line and the faucet, for example. It was frustrating. Kind of like kneeling beside your car, placing your hands underneath the car as far as they will go, and then building a model airplane. Well, the new flexible hoses do away with that frustration.

Not to say that there is no frustration with plumbing. I had the main floor bathroom sink all installed and turned the water back on. Soon, one of the children said, "Hey, Daddy, it's leaking under there!" That wasn't music to my ears. I got a wrench and retightened everything up. Still, a water drop slowly developed and then came crashing down. I figured out that it was coming from the waste line. Because we had installed a pedestal sink (with hidden plumbing) it was a little harder to tighten up the nuts on the drain pipe (remember my word picture of building a model airplane under a car?). Patience. That is what plumbing takes. Lots of patience. And for some reason, it is harder for me to have patience working on something like leaky plumbing if a couple of children are hanging around. You know how children will just sort of watch you while they slurrrrrrppppppp their popsicle, or toss a beanbag near your head and drop it accidentally, knocking over your can of putty. I don't know about you but that can drive me absolutely bonkers!

I finally got the leak stopped, but fully expected a child to come running gleefully (at least that is the way they look to me when they bring bad news), "Daddy, it's leaking again. Guess you didn't fix it!" But they didn't come running. The leaks were all stopped. Have been for a year now. I'm amazed and thankful. It really is possible to do your own plumbing.

I brought the new toilet into the house and started to put it together. Again, no problem. Just take your time and read the directions thoroughly. That's something I always do. I didn't learn it from my dad, however. He always just put something together without reading directions and then would usually end up with a handful of parts left over. Well, I read the directions about installing the toilet and they clearly stated, "DO NOT OVER TIGHTEN THE BOLTS HOLDING THE TOILET TO

THE FLOOR!" Question. How much do you have to tighten before you "over tighten?" The directions didn't tell me. They just told me not to over tighten. So, I tightened the bolts a little bit, and then stopped to see if the toilet was tight enough. Since it would rock from side to side about 3 inches, I decided the bolts were probably not tight enough. I kept tightening and checking, tightening and checking. Never did know when I was going to stop. You see, as you tighten these bolts, you are causing a thick wax seal to smash down between the toilet and the drain pipe. So, the resistance you feel almost right away is just that wax seal getting smashed. Finally, with beads of perspiration forming on my brow (from fear of OVER TIGHTENING) I stopped and walked away. A few days later I noticed water seeping out of the bottom of the toilet. I tightened some more, which seemed to stop the leak. Honestly, can't they come up with a better system of instructions than just telling you not to OVER TIGHTEN? The company that invents fail-safe tightening bolts or writes more meaningful instructions is going to go places.

Bathroom flooring. Now I am into the realm of stuff that can't go wrong. Well, not exactly. The existing flooring was ceramic tile with the usual pieces of cracked tiles here and there. One option was to remove the tile, put in a sheet of plywood, and then install the new flooring over it. The other option, according to a tile shop I visited, was to apply a concrete-kind-of surface on top of the tile, and then lay the new flooring right on top of that. I chose the second option as easier and more cost-effective. I bought the tile-covering "goop" and drove home.

That night, after the children were in bed, I read the directions for the "goop" carefully. They said that once I mixed the solution with water I would have 30 minutes to use it before it would get totally hard. That's pressure! Even though the area of my bath was small, I still didn't like knowing that I only had 30 minutes. What if something went wrong? To reduce the chances of something going wrong, I read and reread the directions. I had everything laid out so I could get to it easily. I was, in short, totally prepared for whatever could go wrong. I was using my Boy Scout training of being prepared. Or so I thought.

I got a bucket to mix this "goop" in and poured the powder in. Then I got another bucket of water and told Susie to look at the clock and remember when I started mixing. I would only have 30 minutes and she was to give me periodic "time-left" updates. With nothing else to prevent me from starting, I poured the water into the mixing bucket.

Instantly I saw that I was going to have a problem. When the water hit that powder it turned the consistency of hard rubber. It was just about everything I could do to move my stirrer once around the bucket. And I could see that it was going to take a lot of work and time to get it mixed thoroughly. I began to sweat. My arms got tired. I could feel time ticking away. Susie said "20 minutes left." I was still mixing! How was I going to get it mixed and spread in twenty minutes?

Finally, I said, "Enough!" You remember those old Western movies when the good guys (always a small number) who are trapped inside a farmhouse, are getting all shot up by the bad guys (always a large number)? Suddenly the good guys decide that "enough is enough" and they storm out of the house shooting their six-shooters in a burst of bravery (and a good bit of idiocy). Well, I stormed into the bathroom and started shooting this "goop" all over the floor in a similar burst of bravery (and in a similar burst of idiocy).

"Fifteen minutes left," Susie said calmly, from the living room where she was reading. As I spread the goop I suddenly realized something else I hadn't considered before. My little pointed cement trowel was not going to give me the perfectly smooth surface that my new flooring demanded. I needed a wide straight trowel to provide the finish I needed. The more I worked, the more valleys and mountains I created with that goop. Honestly, it would have been funny if it hadn't been so sad! "Five minutes left," Susie said as she walked to the bathroom door to watch me. "Is that the way it's supposed to look?" she asked with a surprised look on her face.

In five short minutes, I was through. Oh, that "goop" wasn't smooth, not by a long shot. But it was already too hard to work with. With a sense of failure and frustration I went to bed.

Somehow I imagined that when I walked downstairs in the morning that gravity or perhaps the hole in the ozone layer would have miraculously made the "goop" smooth. It hadn't. Every mountain and valley was still very much there for many amazed young eyes to behold. So I grabbed some sandpaper and started sanding it smooth. After a few minutes of sanding I stopped to take a break. I calculated that if I sanded, nonstop, I could get the floor perfectly smooth by the year 2010. I then secured "bigger guns" and brought my electric belt sander in. However, it seemed to eat too much of the "goop" away so I was back to hand tools. With the help of a hand planer I was able to get some semblance of smoothness. Which means, instead of valleys and mountains, I had ditches and foothills. Oh well, it was the best I was going to do. I was tired of messing with that "goop" and wanted to cover it up with flooring. How big a difference could it make anyway?

To cut the vinyl flooring correctly I made a full-size pattern from a piece of stiff paper. This was necessary because the room wasn't square, and because I had to cut out for the toilet drain and for the shape of the old-fashioned tub. I took the pattern, face side up, and placed it on top of the flooring, which was also face side up. It's important that you do this correctly. My dad bought a piece of very expensive carpeting for our bathroom at home when I was a child. He carefully drew and cut out a pattern of his bathroom floor, just like I did. He then took it to his carpet, but instead of putting it on top of the carpet, he turned the carpet over and then laid his pattern down. Thus, the carpet was face side down, while the pattern was face side up. He marked the carpet, and carefully cut it. All of this measuring and attention to detail was unusual for my dad who had much less patience than I have! Then, whistling I do believe, he carried the carpet to the bathroom. It was a perfect fit! Only problem was that for it to fit perfectly it had to be laid upside down! Thus, the beautiful side of the carpet was facing down and the ugly backing was what was staring him in the face. Dad staggered out of the bathroom moaning, "I'm sick. I'm sick." Twister, our dog, ended up with that piece of carpet for her doghouse. My dad always said she had the most expensive flooring of any dog in the Chattanooga area! The moral of the story is to think, and lay your pattern on top of your flooring with both pieces facing the same direction.

My flooring appeared to fit well, so it was time to secure it to my "ocean" of dips and hills. This was a new type of flooring from Armstrong, and instead of putting the glue all over the floor, you were supposed to just put a band of glue about three inches wide around the perimeter of the room. Shucks, I had enough glue to glue the whole floor. Why not do that? Wouldn't that make a better adhesion? Wouldn't I have the best adhered floor around? I must admit that I tend to live by the philosophy that says if a little glue is good, a lot of glue must be great! After thinking about it awhile, I chose not to put the glue all over the floor and trust the manufacturer. But I must say that I put a band of glue of about six inches around the perimeter instead of three. Surely that wouldn't hurt.

As the days went by, I noticed that the flooring was starting to stretch tighter. That is what it was supposed to do. Sad to say, those little "hills and ditches" showed through the flooring. Oh well, by the time they cause a puncture in the flooring, it will probably be time to replace the flooring anyway. I have tried not to let it bother me. That's another thing I have had to learn. When you are finished with a job, just let it be! Don't always be going over to it and thinking about the things you goofed up. Be happy about the things you have done right. Again, that's hard for my personality to do. Rick Ridnour, a good friend of mine, has a very positive attitude about life and the things that happen in life, and he has helped me to see how important it is to look on the bright side of things. I doubt if I'll ever get to where Rick is, but it is nice to have a role model for the traits you are trying to achieve in life. God has brought many wonderful people into my life to help me become who He wants me to be.

Fixing up the basement bathroom was a lot less work. That bathroom is used mostly when people have muddy boots, etc. It does have the only shower in the house, however, so we wanted it to be a little more "finished" than it was. I scrubbed the walls and painted them with enamel paint. I also painted the "ceiling" (which is just the floor joists from the floor above) with white enamel paint so that we could clean it easily if it ever got mildewy. I installed an additional light next to the shower so it wouldn't be so dark while someone is showering. That, plus the white ceiling, really added a lot of light to the room, making it a more inviting place to shower. With all of that light, you can more easily spot the spiders that hide in the shower.

I had a few pieces of vinyl flooring left from the main floor bathroom and decided to install them in the basement bathroom. But first, I had to repair the subflooring which had several holes in it due to rotting (looked like people never shut the shower curtain when they showered!). I drove to the lumber yard and bought a new piece of 3/4 inch plywood. I wanted a strong floor with no joints, so I cut out a pattern of the current floor. After tracing the pattern onto the plywood I cut it out and carried it to the basement.

At first it wouldn't fit. Oh, sure it would go through the door. But there wasn't enough clearance due to the location of the shower and sink to lay it down in one piece. Now when something like that happens to me, I just figure it is because I have not carefully thought it through. Have I looked at every possible way to do this? I worked and sweated, and sweated and worked with that heavy piece of plywood for quite a long while before realizing that it was impossible for it to fit. I finally had to cut it into two pieces to be able to get it wedged into the right position. The moral: Sometimes things cannot work the way you want them to. Be willing to admit that and move on.

Two more things needed work in the basement bathroom: the toilet was leaking (inside itself, not on the floor) and the sink was stained, ugly, and inconvenient (it had a separate hot faucet and cold faucet--impossible to mix the two and get good warm water!) Of course, it was really old-fashioned, so Susie loved it and was sorry to see it go, but a man has to draw the line somewhere. The toilet was fixed by visiting the hardware store and buying all new parts that go into the tank. Only problem was that I apparently tightened the new part too tight, causing a hairline crack. This hairline crack in the metal allowed water to run out of the tank continuously. It wasn't until several days later that I noticed water marks on the walls outside the bathroom and knew I had a leak. It was a very slow leak, but such a leak can make a big mess over the course of a few days. After replacing the part with a new one (and I didn't OVER TIGHTEN it!) the toilet was in good shape. That left the sink.

At a yard sale I found a good serviceable sink for $2.50. It had a good faucet installed and had no rust. I bought it! When I tried to install it, I learned why the guy had apparently sold it. It leaked. Not in one place but in two places. When I looked around to see if I could replace the faucet I learned that this was some kind of "special order" faucet, and not the kind you can pick up for $30-$40. So I started trying to stop those leaks. It was kind of like assembling a model airplane with my hands under a car again! I tried to enjoy the process but was not totally success-ful. However, I did keep my cool a lot more than I ever had before. It helped to be working in the cool basement on a hot day. I hope I had also learned to be a little more relaxed when doing that kind of stuff. I solved both leaks by using some o-rings, but not where o-rings had ever been before. Time will tell if they hold up. If not, I'll go out and buy a brand new sink and faucet, something I probably should have done in the first place.

Building a chimney and installing a woodburning stove

At the beginning of this chapter I sort of "left you hanging" with me on a slippery roof, trying to finish laying a chimney. Let me back up and set the stage. Susie had always wanted a wood burning stove in her kitchen. Yet we didn't have a chimney with access in the kitchen. We could have hired it done, but Robin said it wasn't hard at all to build a chimney and that he would gladly provide some guidance if I decided to build one.

After thinking it over, I decided, "Why not?" Susie and I chose some bricks and brought them home in Robin's truck. I bought some cement, mason's sand, and chimney flue, and brought them home in the back of my van. We were ready. Only problem is that it was already winter time.   We didn't want to wait, though, because we had already secured an ancient wood burning stove (meaning that it was old-fashioned and cute) and Susie was anxious to start using it. Also, I was looking forward to the heat it would add to the house.

At first I thought I would have to start building the chimney on the floor of the basement, in order to have a strong foundation. Robin, however, said it would be okay just to start on the kitchen floor with the chimney. All it would require was the addition of a metal support beam under that area in the basement. That saved me a lot of work and material--10 feet of material to be exact, because that is the height of our basement!

Before starting to lay the brick, I dropped plumb lines (using a string and a weighted metal point) from the ceiling of the kitchen to the kitchen floor and nailed them in place. I would use these lines to make sure the outside corners of the chimney remained square. The plan called for a brick wall, about six feet wide and five feet high, to serve as a fire wall behind the chimney. The chimney itself would be 16" x 16", with an 8" x 8" chimney flue inside.

I then moved some bricks into the kitchen and mixed the mortar (following the directions on the package in terms of the sand-to-concrete ratio). A level area of mortar about 3/8" thick was placed on the floor and served as the only "foundation" needed. The bricks were then laid on top of this still-wet mortar foundation.

Several things I learned right away.   It is harder to put the mud (meaning mortar) on the brick than it looks. Sure, you can slap some on, but will it be the right amount and will it stay on? In terms of amount, that is just a trial and error thing and depends on how wide you are going to space your bricks from each other. I spaced mine 3/8" apart. But how do you get that mud to stay on the brick? After you scoop up some mud and slather it on the end of your brick, you then tap the edge of the brick with your trowel. That simple motion will usually do the trick and cause the mud to adhere long enough to put the brick in place.

Okay, several problems were solved, but a new one popped

up. It seemed like just about as soon as I laid down a layer of mud and starting laying a few bricks on top, that the mud dried out too quickly on me. I was left with a crumbly mess of mortar that I was not too hopeful would actually hold the bricks together. After a call to Robin, I was okay. He told me that the reason for my problem was that the bricks were too dry. This seemed reasonable since I had stored the ones I was going to use inside the warm house for a few days. Since they were dry, they were wicking the moisture right out of the mud. The solution was a simple one. Just get a five-gallon bucket, fill it about ⅔ of the way with water, and fill it with bricks. In a few minutes the bricks will have absorbed all the water they can absorb, and won't have any need or desire to suck more water out of the mud. It worked!

My only problem now was to make sure that I kept the walls and chimney straight. With the help of the plumb lines, that was made somewhat easier, but I still had to step back after each course (that just means one layer of bricks) and make sure it was still looking okay. If you're not careful you'll slowly lay the bricks out of plumb because the string will stretch to where your bricks are laid. I must have forgotten to check on a few courses, probably because I was in a hurry (hard winter was rapidly approaching). Anyway, the result is that I can now (and my great-grandchildren can 150 years from now) look at the brick wall and see where three or four courses dip to the right. Oh, well, it is not all that noticeable and not a big deal. Besides, someday after I am long gone, maybe one of my children or grandchildren will look at that, and with a tear in their eye say, "That mistake was made by Grand-daddy! I sure miss him."

I built the fire wall and chimney nearly to the kitchen ceiling. Then the really hard work began. I had to go up into the attic space and lay many layers of brick. This is hard for several reasons. First, I no longer had any plumb lines to work from. Of course, it didn't matter much because no one was going to go into my attic and see if the bricks were straight. But I found myself getting a little too much "off," resulting in the space between bricks reaching 3/4 of an inch at times. Second, it was harder to work in the attic because the head room was almost nonexistent. Even though it was cold weather it still felt stuffy to me, probably because it was so cramped up there.   Third, it was less fun, because I didn't have a "cheerleader squad" anymore.   While I was working in the kitchen, the children or Susie would often stop by and watch my progress.   Those "Boy, that sure looks good, Steve!" comments were an encouragement.   In the attic, I still had occasional visitors, but not as often and not for as long. We really didn't want the children breathing the insulation that was up there.   Oh, the loneliness of a man working in the attic!

As I neared the top of the attic (the underside of the roof), I became much less sure of myself.   I was getting better at laying brick; that wasn't the problem.   My fear was to cut a hole in the roof for the chimney to extend through.   For some reason, it seemed about as big of a deal for me to cut a hole in my roof as it would be to, say, take the transmission out of the only car we had and try to replace it.   When I cut that hole, I knew that I was then committing myself to finish this project, one way or another, in the next several days.   Since it was winter, I was not thrilled with the prospects of upcoming bad weather.   Besides, what if I cut that hole in the roof, got sick with the flu for several days, and we had a bad snowstorm?   Wouldn't all that snow come drifting into my attic and my house?   Yes it would!   See my fear?

But persistence won out over fear.   In fact I've come to the conclusion that persistence is about the best thing you can have when it comes to do-it-yourself projects.   You can't be afraid to start a job. And you can't give up.   You have to keep working at it until it is done.   At least that's the way it is for me.

I cut the hole.   Actually, it was a lot more work than that little four word sentence would indicate.   I couldn't just crawl up on the roof, try to measure where to cut and start cutting.   On one side I was real close to a ceiling joist and I didn't want to saw it in two.   So, I started this part of the job by working from the inside.   I used a board to see where the chimney should extend out of the attic, and marked it.   Then I drilled four holes, one at each corner of where the chimney would go.   I then went outside, on the top of the roof, and used a saw to cut from hole to hole, making a square about 16" x 16", the size of the chimney. I tried to be careful when removing the shingles because I didn't want to have to patch in a lot of new shingles once the job was over.

Now that I had a gaping hole in my roof, I felt even more pressure to get those bricks laid fast so that I could patch around the remaining space. I got to work and threw those bricks down pretty fast. It was especially hard when I got very close to the roofline. It was too close to work from the inside anymore, so outside into the cold I headed.

I set up some scaffolding braces to hold the ten-inch board I was going to work from. These braces were just nailed into the roof with 20 penny nails. Would they support all my weight and the weight of my bricks and mortar? I had some real doubts, even though everyone said they would. Already the height was starting to worry me. I wasn't that high off the ground, but my fear of heights magnified it probably threefold!

I carried bricks (soaking in a bucket of water), mortar, and my tools to the roof and began to lay bricks. I suddenly realized a problem. I had made the opening exactly 16" x 16" but I needed it wider in order to have a slight air space between the bricks (which might get hot) and the wood. So I had to drag up a saw again and cut more of the roof away. Even though it doesn't sound like a big deal, it was eating up time. And dark clouds were starting to form overhead. Snow clouds. Also, Susie wasn't home. Now I didn't expect her to do anything with regard to this project. But she is my partner and best friend and in times of worry or fear I just like to know she is really close by.

After cutting the roof away, I laid a few more courses of bricks. It started snowing. Not knowing how many days it would be before I could return to work up there, I carried all my tools down. I also placed into position a piece of aluminum sheeting to help divert any snow or melted snow away from the crack between the chimney and the wood of the roof. Finally, I wrapped the chimney with a piece of tarp. This was not only to keep the snow out. It also served to keep the inside of the chimney warm (with somewhat warm air from the attic pouring up the chimney), which was supposed to help the mortar dry and cure properly.

I worked on the chimney off and on for several days as the snow and my schedule allowed. I noticed that the chimney was sort of taking a shape all its own. I had no way to drop a plumb line (from where, a cloud?) and thus was relying on using a level to try and keep the chimney straight on all four sides. I was failing miserably! The chimney sort of looked like a screw, twisting counterclockwise as it climbed upward. Oh, well, who would ever see it anyway? Thankfully it was on the back of the house.

Due to the escaping heat from the attic, I now had some ice on the roof to contend with in addition to the snow. I was not real excited about the way I slid occasionally while working on the roof. To put my mind more at ease, I devised a sort of safety rope out of chain that was lying in the barn. It constricted my movements, and occasionally caused me to get tangled up, but it did give me some peace of mind. I knew if I slipped, the chain would keep me from falling off the roof, that is if it didn't cause the whole chimney to just come crashing down with me!

Finally, a day came when I was almost finished with laying the bricks. It was very cold outside. I toyed with the idea of not working that day, but decided against it because there was no guarantee that it wouldn't just get colder. That day is related in the narrative at the beginning of this chapter. How did it turn out, you might ask? Let me tell you.

I didn't fall off. Sorry. I know that would have made for a much more interesting story, but it didn't happen. (I'll see what I can do in the future about falling off so that sequels to this book can be more exciting for you.) What did happen is that Robin showed up. Why he came over, I'll never know. Perhaps he was driving by and he saw me on the roof. A lot of people had. Many honked. Some just looked in disbelief. Why would Steve be on his roof in December building a chimney?

Anyway, Robin dropped by. In characteristic-Robin style, he climbed the ladder and asked if he could help. He wasn't dressed for this work. He had no gloves on. But he asked if he could help. I'm sorry, but I was in a pretty desperate situation and I said, "YES!" He took those bricks and laid the last three or four rows with skill and grace that I've never seen excelled by professional brick layers. His rows were straight and true. The amount of mortar between bricks was consistent. The only thing I "regret" about his helping is that the last four rows don't match the rest of the chimney. His rows were straight and mine were, well, kind of like a screw.

I placed a big bead of roofing cement around the chimney to keep snow and melted ice out of the attic until spring, when I planned on installing flashing around the chimney. (Actually, Jeff installed the flashing for me in the spring.) I covered the chimney with the tarp and carried my tools down. I also inserted a 100-watt bulb in the base of the chimney, through the clean-out door. Even though it didn't put off tons of heat, it did provide enough heat to help the mortar cure properly.

I cleaned myself up and absolutely flew to school (remember I had a meeting to attend). I got there about 10 minutes late and raced down the hall to the meeting place. When I entered, the faculty were just getting ready to stand up and leave. "Where are you going?" I asked. "Is the meeting already over? I'm only 10 minutes late!" "Well, we decided that we didn't have anything to meet about. You really should have a car phone, Steve, and then we could just call to tell you that you don't need to come on in for a meeting if we change our minds." I had rushed for nothing. It's not the first time, and probably won't be the last time either. Our society needs to slow down. Me included.

Other stuff inside the house

I have done a lot of other stuff inside the house. For example, I installed a new hot water heater. The only thing new for me about that was "sweating" the pipes. That just means that you heat the pipe and solder the joints with some soldering paste. Somehow I had elevated that job to the exclusive domain of the professional plumber. There was just no way I could sweat pipes and make them watertight, or so I thought. Robin, though, said that of course I could. So I tried. It worked great. I already owned a small propane blow torch and only had to buy a new cylinder of propane. I also bought a "starter's kit" that included solder, flux (the stuff you clean your pipes with before you solder them), a few brushes (to apply the flux with), and some emery cloth (to sand the metal and get it clean where you are going to solder). The nice thing is that the back of the starter kit gave some clear directions on how to "sweat" the pipe. I followed them exactly and it worked perfectly. No leaks and nothing had to be done over.

We also had some wall and ceiling damage in the upstairs due to ice building up on the eaves of the house. This effectively blocks runoff water which then seeps through the shingles, running down the interior walls. To fix that I installed some of those "ice melt" wires on the places of the roof that have very low slopes (the dormers). Then when the outside temperature gets around 20 degrees and the snow on the roof starts to melt, I simply plug in these units. That solved my water damage problems.

Cleaning chimneys is one chore that is required when maintaining a farmhouse. I have two chimneys that operate from about early September until sometime in June (it depends upon when summer actually arrives here). I'm afraid of heights. And heights that contain snow and ice on an angle are even more frightening to me. Yet those chimneys need to be cleaned every month or two or the creosote can build up and cause a chimney fire. By the grace of God, I noticed at the building supply house one day some fiberglass rods for sale. These rods can be attached to your chimney cleaning brush and then inserted up into the chimney from the clean-out (you know, where you get the ashes out) in the house. The fiberglass is flexible enough to bend a lot and thus make that initial 90 degree turn up the chimney. Now from the safety (and warmth) of the inside of my house, I can clean my complete chimney even when it is 40 below zero outside and three feet of ice and snow cover my roof. Like I say, I am very thankful for some modern inventions!

Chapter 12
Getting the Outbuildings In Shape

W hen we first moved in, a total of 576 square feet was being added to the house (to end up with a 1632 square foot "bungalow") by a contractor. Since they seemed to be making enough noise on their own, I decided to start working in other areas of the farm. The two-car garage seemed a logical place.

The Garage

Fixing up the garage would have been a simple job of scraping, priming, and putting on two coats of paint. Would have been, that is, if the garage had ever been finished. You might think that this garage was built just before we moved in, which would explain why some of the siding had not been installed. Actually, I've been told that it was built by some renters more than 10 years earlier. They apparently didn't think about the fact that you can't easily move a 25' x 27' building with a concrete floor when you stop renting. Thankfully, and unbelievably to me, the rest of the siding was still on the garage floor, gathering dust.

Installing siding is not hard. Just snap a straight line to make sure you are putting it on straight, then nail it on. It is easier if you have a few helpers to hold the twenty-foot lengths of siding, but I put some on without any help (I didn't say they were straight!). The only really hard part was cutting the angles at the top so it would fit perfectly under the roof line. To cut these I made a template, which is just a piece of junk wood cut to the right angle. This angle was then traced onto the siding, and then the siding was cut and nailed on.

The Hen House

Having the garage in pretty good shape, I next looked to my hen house (which was later to be called our chick house). I noticed that although the hens weren't complaining, there were a few things that needed to be done. For one thing, the roof was in very bad condition. Along about that same time, we were shopping at a salvage yard for some inexpensive house-building materials. The owner, pointing to a large stack of shingles, said we could have any of them that we wanted: for FREE! So we loaded up our little trailer with free shingles and headed home.

Installing shingles over old ones is easy. Just start at the bottom and nail right on top of the ones that are there. I have since learned, after working with better shingles, that the ones I put on the hen house are painfully thin and cheap. Sort of makes me wish I had just bought some new shingles. However, the hen house has never leaked in the last three years and the shingles look to have some life left in them yet.

I also worried about my hens because winter was rapidly approaching. Would they freeze to death? Although people said they wouldn't, I didn't really believe them. I had some used insulation that I had removed from the basement ceiling. The reason I removed it from the basement was that it looked like it could hold moisture and mold. Anyway, I used this stuff to insulate the hen house. As I was to learn later, that was not a good decision. The hen house, since it was closed up tight, could not "breathe." Water condensed on the walls. That's not a good situation if you want healthy chickens. So, down came the insulation. See what I mean about things never being finished on a farm?

Dan Siler had given me some old windows and an old sliding glass door panel, and I had an idea. Why not cut a huge hole in the south end (back) of the hen house and put the sliding glass door panel there? The window would take up about 90% of the back of the house. That would give the hens the south sun all winter long and keep the house somewhat warm. So, that's what I did. It worked, too. The only problem is in the warmth of summer, when the window heats up the house. It's not a big problem, though, because the hens are let out during the day in summer anyway. Also, we have windows that open for ventilation.

The Milk House

What to do with the old milk house? Although its size, 16' x 12', might make it seem worthy of repair, several factors played against it. The original part of the building had had an 8' x 12' addition that was not built with great care or maintained lovingly. The roof was leaking and caving in, the foundation was crumbling and terribly cracked, the concrete floor was heaved up and cracked, the walls were crumbling (and could be caused to sway back and forth with just your fingers), the windows were all broken out, and a swarm of yellow jackets had set up permanent quarters inside the rotting structure. I must admit that my first reaction was to tear it down. So that's what we did.

If you want to make good friends with children, just hand them a hammer or a crowbar or a sledgehammer or a mattock and tell them, "Just do anything that comes natural to you." At first, the children were reluctant and eyed me cautiously. All those years of training them to be civilized had really paid off. Finally they said, "Do you mean we can *hit* this building?" "Yes, like this," I said, and demonstrated by crashing into the wall with my sledgehammer. With that demonstration, they tore into the building with gusto. Joy! Bliss! Ecstasy! Fun! And occasionally a scratch. It took us several days to demolish the building.

The children found all sorts of "treasures" as we were ripping up the milk house. One was a 72-year-old letter written in a foreign language. We could hardly wait to see what it said. The children were hoping it told something neat about life on this old farm. You know, something like, "We took the draft horses to the blacksmith today . . ." I was hoping it said something like, "The gold is buried near the old . . ." One day, Mrs. Mrs. Berglund was at the farm, so we asked her if she knew what language the letter was written in. No, that's not a typo. Inez

Berglund is called Mrs. Mrs. by my children, because her daughter-in-law, Marlene, is called Mrs. Berglund. Makes perfect sense you see. If Mrs. Mrs. Berglund's mother-in-law were still living, I suppose she would be called Mrs. Mrs. Mrs. Berglund.

Anyway, she verified our hunch that it was written in Finnish. Since this is a Finnish area, it wasn't hard to get the letter translated. Grandma Bev's mother did the honors. I know you just can't wait to hear the translation, so here it is in its entirety:

> I'm getting out Saturday of this week. If you could come here the whole family. We'll go someplace from here if it works out. I will fix food package. Could you call somebody here Saturday morning or else Friday evening? If you're home. Don't plan on going anywhere next Saturday. I'll see Armaa before then. Armaa and Emil will find the place.

Even though translated, it's still a mystery to me. Sounds like someone is "getting out" (of the house or jail?), and is going to rendezvous with a few old "friends" on Saturday at . . . , well, they know the place. I'm still looking for the gold. If only Armaa or Emil were still around . . .

Other gems in the milk house included a huge two foot milk thermometer, a small carved wooden thing, both one cent stamps from the old letter, half of a rusty vise, an old sign that reads "**FIRST** USE THE OLDEST," some dilapidated rubber parts of a milk machine, some old rusty cans, the skull of a squirrel or rat, a piece of really thin metal that looked like gold, about four pounds of rusty nails and bolts, some pieces of broken glass, and other neat stuff. A lot of this ended up in the house, until Susie and I found out about it. We have a rule at our house about "treasures." They can either stay in one part of the barn earmarked for that purpose, or they can stay in a child's "treasure" (shoe) box. If they want to put something new in their treasure box, something has to go. With regards to treasures in the old milk house, I am just glad we didn't find what Robin said might be in there--old blasting caps for dynamite which many people stored in their milk house in the old days. Wouldn't that be neat to find, perhaps as the result of a swing with the old sledge hammer? BOOM!

After tearing down the milk house we were left with the crumbling foundation and concrete floor. We would like to get rid of it because it's not a safe place for children to play. There are old rusty nails and bolts sticking out of the concrete foundation walls, and the floors are heaving up so badly that they are almost 100% guaranteed child-tripper. What do you do with something like that? It would be too much work to pound it out with a sledge hammer. I suppose I could rent a pneumatic jackhammer. Even if we had a bulldozer come in, what would we do with the material? This seems to be a problem others have too, because we've seen the concrete remains of old buildings on many farms we've visited. If anyone out there has a use for a bunch of old concrete, let me know!

The Shop

The shop supplied many a work-filled day too. Structurally, it was in good shape, but the entire outside had to be scraped, primed and painted. We also had to finish siding its back side. Seems like some folks don't see a need to put siding where visitors don't normally venture, even though the weather still takes its toll back there!

The shop roof had seemed in pretty good shape when we moved in. In fact, it almost looked new. When it rained, however, we realized that it was anything but new. The leaks were large and constant. When I climbed up on the roof, I learned that the roof was painted. The shingles were actually so old that they crumbled in my hand. Thus, the older children got to use their budding demolition skills again, by tearing off a very rotten layer of shingles. It's a dirty, messy job, and can be dangerous with all those nails, some still sticking through a small piece of roofing, laying all over the ground. The solution? Robin suggested that we tie a magnet on a string and let some of the little children sort of fish around on the ground for nails. The children had a ball doing that ("No. It's *my* turn. You've had a long time playing with the magnet . . . ")! And the good news is that I have never had a flat tire around that building because the nails were all removed. A simple and very effective solution to a troubling mess. Thanks, Robin!

After the shingles were removed, I discovered that part of the roof was rotten. Always count on a job to cost more than you expected! Seems like just about everything I have worked on has ended up taking a bit more time and money than what I originally planned. I tore off the rotten wood, replaced it with plywood, and applied tar paper to the entire roof. Then I attached a special three-foot wide rubber roll roofing to the edge of the roof, a necessary addition up here in snow country to keep ice from backing up under your shingles and ruining your roof when the ice melts. After adding a metal drip guard to support the edge of the shingles that hang over, it was time to put on new shingles. I had learned my lesson on the hen house and decided to buy top-of-the-line shingles, which also matched those on my house. Installing shingles on a shingle-less roof is still an easy job. Directions come right on the package of shingles that you buy. You simply snap a chalk line where you want the top of the first course of shingles to lay and start hammering them on. After completing the first course, you snap another chalk line, taking into account the amount of overlap you desire. You start at the lowest place on your roof and work upward. The shingle packaging tells you how to end up with all sorts of patterns that you might desire. I went with one of the simplest patterns possible because it matched my house roof.

My final act in the shop was to add a small wood-burning stove. I had tried to use an electric heater but it just couldn't heat the shop and was cost-prohibitive. I couldn't work out there without continually thinking about the electric meter whizzing around faster and faster! Then I tried to use a kerosene stove. No whizzing meter thoughts flashed through my brain. In fact, sometimes it seemed like nothing was pulsing through my brain. It just wasn't good for my health to be breathing those exhaust fumes. I would come back into the house to eat lunch, but everything tasted like kerosene exhaust. Wood-burning stoves use a very cheap fuel that I have lots of - wood. And since they have to be vented to the outside, my mind should stay clearer. So I installed a wood-burner. It has turned out to be very effective at raising the temperature fast and creating a comfortable environment. I have been able to work in my shop even though it was 20° below zero right outside the door. It helps make the shop a nice, warm place for the children to get out of the house and reduce cabin fever. I highly recommend a wood-burner.

The Barn

It was now time to move my fix-up tools and thoughts to the barn. I must admit that I was somewhat reluctant to start in the barn. Its size was kind of overwhelming to me and there seemed to be lots of things I needed to do. The first thing I did was to tear out all of the electrical wiring and the old fuse box, and install new wiring and a new circuit breaker box. I've heard of too many neat, old barns going up in flames due to faulty wiring. I used nothing but Type UF waterproof cable for wiring, even though it is more expensive and harder to work with, because it offers superior protection in wet and damp locations. All of the electrical outlets were tied into special protection circuits, called ground fault circuit interrupters or GFCI, like the kind you may have in your bathroom. These circuits are more expensive, but much safer in barn-type conditions. If someone (like one of my children) accidentally "gets into" the hot wire, the current will be cut off in about a fortieth of a second - a shock so brief that it won't harm them. What is the value of the life of one of your children or yourself? Go with GFCI!

When it was time to hook all of the wires into the new electrical box, I heard all kinds of comments from family and friends, like "Are you sure you know what you're doing?" "Couldn't you just let an electrician do it?" "Have you ever done anything like this before?" etc. I did try to get an electrician out. He promised to give me an estimate but he never showed up. So I decided to do it myself. I should mention that I am not totally a novice when it comes to electricity. When I was nine years old, I helped my Uncle John, who was an electrician, do some wiring of houses. Now, I'm not sure what I remember from when I was nine, but I do have confidence that electrical work can be done by nonelectrician people like me. You have to decide if you have confidence to tackle a job like this.

The first thing I did was to kill all incoming power. It's imperative to hook up the wires into the box correctly and tightly. There are many books that explain how to do this. If you read the books and still don't understand, then don't do it yourself. Get someone who knows what they are doing. It really is not that difficult, however. I just make sure I take my time and check/recheck with a voltage meter to make sure a line is dead before I touch it.

It gets dark early up here in northern Wisconsin in the winter. That can make it harder to do chores outside the barn (like water and hay). So we added a few outside lights to illuminate these areas. It sure is a lot easier than carrying a bale of hay around while trying to hold a flashlight under your chin!

The main floor of the barn was not really useful to me because it had about 50 iron stanchions up and down both sides. I was not interested in milking 50 cows and wanted to get the stanchions out. First, I tried to knock them out with a sledgehammer. I was even able to knock one or two loose ones out, with a great deal of effort. But the rest just wouldn't budge. If you want to feel really weak, just try pounding on heavy iron as hard as you can, with your children standing near saying, "Is it about to come out yet, Daddy?" When you consider that these stanchions were designed to keep a 1500 pound cow just where you want her, it's not really surprising that they would be made tough. I mentioned my predicament to my neighbor, Todd Bitner, who said he would be glad to remove them for the scrap iron. And he did. In one afternoon he and his dad, Martin Bitner, were able to use their oxygen/acetylene torch and cut them off at their base.   They got the iron, and I got a large area of my barn stanchion-free. A pretty good deal.   I was out less than $50, which was used to help defray the costs of refilling their oxygen tank (they really didn't want to take the money).

Even though the stanchions were gone, the concrete base that held them in place was still there. These are about six inches wide and about six inches high off the floor, with another six inches imbedded in the concrete floor. I assume these stanchion bases were poured before the concrete floor was poured. Now how am I going to get rid of the bases? Sledgehammers, goggles, and sweat. The fact that a good deal of each one is "under" the floor, like an iceberg, doesn't make it easy to dislodge them. I haven't knocked them all out yet. Sort of hoping someone will come along and want the concrete for free and be willing to take it out. I've an idea I will be waiting for a long time. Even when you do knock them out you are still left with a problem: what to do with the resulting 6" deep, 6" wide cavity you've created in the floor. It's a great place for old hay and manure to "hide."

The barn was also in need of some serious window repair/replacement. Most window openings just had boards, foam insulation, and/or sheetrock covering them. The barn had about 20 windows on the main floor, making it cost prohibitive to buy new ones. I was blessed that several people gave me pieces of old windows in various sizes and shapes. These were repaired, reglazed and then attached to plywood or wooden slats I had assembled to fill in the window opening completely. A few were placed on hinges so that the window could be opened. Since I mostly used wood that had been lying around the place, the total costs were relatively low. My only real expenses were for hinges, a little wood, glass glazing material, paint, and my time. Winter is a good time to make windows, since there is not much else you can do on the farm. However, it's hard to get glazing to set properly in 20° below zero weather.

I also had eight windows to repair/replace in the hayloft area of the barn. Some were 24 feet above the hayloft floor! I'm a rather cautious person.   Translation: I'm scared to death of heights. I got a few of the windows removed, but then decided there must be a better way than nearly passing out with "caution" (that is to say, fear). Adam Beckel was willing to do the high work in exchange for bales of hay. It's called barter and I highly recommend it. Adam climbed up the ladder, removed the remaining windows, I repaired them all, and then he reinstalled them. Some people just aren't afraid of heights. If you don't know anyone like that, I suggest you start looking for them.

Now that the windows in the barn loft were fixed, I hoped that the few leaks we were having would go away. After all, the roof looked to be in nearly new condition. However, we still had leaks and it was getting old emptying the five gallon plastic buckets we had set up to catch incoming rain water. There was no way, for any amount of money, that I was going to crawl up on that roof and look around. I wasn't afraid of falling off the top and dying because I knew I would never even make it to the top! My solution was to put a free ad in a local "shopper's paper" (you know, the kind that are nothing but advertisements) seeking someone to do barn roof work. I got two calls. The first man came out, looked at my barn, and never called back. The second contractor, a man I will call Bud, came out and looked it over. I asked for references and if he had liability insurance. He had both. Then I said "How much do you think it will cost me?" He sort of looked up at the barn again, shuffled his feet, kicked a little loose hay, and said, "Oh, I guess about $100 should do it." For that he was going to crawl on the roof, fix any holes, put up extra flashing where the tin roof met the shingles, and generally fix my problem. Should I call his references?

I've learned the importance of not jumping into something without checking it out thoroughly. When I was first out of college in 1979 and a computer salesperson, I needed a nice car. I found a beautiful 1976 Chevrolet Caprice Classic on a used car lot for $3850. That was back when the Caprice was a super-long, extravagant gas-guzzler! The price was so great that I bought it without really checking it out. As I used it I did notice that the gas mileage wasn't great. Then about a month later, my brother Ken needed a ride from Chattanooga, Tennessee to Louisville, Kentucky. "Let's just take my new car," I volunteered. What a trip. We must have stopped for gas at about every other town. The only thing worse is that we stopped for oil more often! I was so disgusted that I sold the Caprice to a car wholesaler in Nashville, Tennessee on the way back home (and lost my shirt in the process!). Two principles I learned: Cut your losses and check things out well ahead of time.

But should I check Bud's references? For just a $100 job it didn't seem necessary. So I didn't.

The day Bud arrived to start work he parked at the end of our driveway and started carrying all of his heavy equipment in by hand. He thought we wouldn't let him drive in because the gate was closed. The children quickly let him know that it was fine if he wanted to drive on in. After he set up, he soon learned that his 40-foot industrial strength ladder wouldn't even reach to the place where the two roofing materials merged. But since he was here, he went ahead and started bending and inserting the flashing. It was a windy day and he was standing on the top rung of his ladder and his ladder was extended just as absolutely far as it would reach. With his hands extended about as far as they would go, he was able to screw the flashing in place. It makes me dizzy just thinking about it. When he came down for a break, he said, "Boy, that's a lot higher than I thought it was going to be. Yeah, boy, that's a lot higher than I thought it was going to be." He worked for about four hours and then decided that he needed more ladders if he was going to get up on the top of the roof.

When Bud returned to finish the job, several weeks later, I noticed that he had brought another ladder along. He used my ladder to get on top of my shed (attached to the barn) and then nailed the 40-foot ladder straight up the side of the barn. Then, he leaned his small ladder up from the top of the large ladder. By crawling up the large ladder, then the small ladder, he was able to make it to the top of the roof. He did attach a safety wire, a fact for which I was grateful, since the wind was blowing strongly. He walked around up there for a good long time, screwing the tin roof into place where it had come dislodged and applying roofing caulk.

Suddenly, the sky grew dark. But not in a storm-kind-of-dark because there was not a cloud in the sky. It got darker and darker. "Boy, I looked around and it got pretty spooky up there for a while. Yeah, pretty spooky up there," Bud related to us later. As it turns out, we were having a solar eclipse, a phenomenon that neither of us knew we were going to have.

What else could go wrong for Bud? Well, a little while later, his cordless drill slipped out of his hand, and it went sliding, sliding, sliding off the tin roof of the barn and landed, SPLAT, on the ground. That could have easily been Bud sliding, sliding, sliding off the barn, because he didn't always hook up his safety cable. Needless to say, it wrecked his drill, so he was through for the day. He came back several times to work on the barn roof. When he was through, I paid him more than his contract called for, because I knew that he had just miscalculated his estimate and I wanted to do the right thing.

The next time it rained, the barn roof still leaked. Not as bad, but it still leaked. Bud had said that there were some .44 caliber holes in some of the roof vents up there. Probably someone up in the hayloft had been taking shots at pigeons in the years gone by. Oh, well, the roof did not leak *as much* and I didn't feel like going through another big deal getting someone out to try and fix it.

Keeping running water in the barn is an area that needs constant attention. We have a pipe that comes up through the concrete and extends about three feet. When we moved in, this pipe had heat tape attached to it. But as I examined it more closely (it was unplugged, thankfully), I learned that the insulation was totally rotten and the bare wires were exposed and touching the metal pipe. It's a wonder a fuse hadn't blown, or worse. I replaced the heat tape, carefully wrapping it in insulation just like the instructions called for. Our barn cats were watching this procedure with a mixture of interest and glee. Wasn't sure about the glee, until later when I realized that they saw this heat tape and insulation as a good scratching post. After reapplying the insulation and making sure the cats had not messed up the heat tape, I wrapped the whole thing up in chicken wire. I hoped that would take away the fun for the cats, and it did. The cats no longer used it as a scratching post.

The only problem was that the water still froze at times. This was because the water was freezing in the faucet itself, a place the heat tape could not reach. I tried several things. First, I wrapped the faucet in a heavy pile of insulation. That kept the faucet from freezing. However, since the heat tape thermostat was near that end, it was kept warm by the insulation and the heat tape would often not come on when it should have. Thus, we had frozen pipes again. Finally, I decided to make a little "house" out of sheets of junk plywood all around the water pipe. This house was 4 feet long, 2 ½ feet wide, and 4 feet high. I then placed hay bales all around and on top of this "house" and installed a 40-watt bulb inside. The water didn't freeze after that. On nights when it was predicted to get really cold (like 20-30° below zero) I replaced the 40 watt bulb with a 100-watt bulb. That solved my problem. (Except when it went to 42° below zero--everyone's barn water froze then!)

Of course I had to get water from the water pipe to the animals' water supply. For the smaller animals, we just ran water into gallon buckets and carried it. For the cows, I placed their stock tank right next to the barn, just outside where the water line comes into the barn. I then installed a ten-foot piece of 4" diameter pipe, sloping downward, on the ceiling of the barn. One end of this pipe was right above the water pipe. The pipe extends through a hole in the barn, and ends right above the cows' water tank. To fill their tank, I simply hook up a short garden hose to the faucet, push it into the pipe and let the water drain downward into the tank. The pipe drains completely so I don't have to worry about it blocking with frozen water. After bleeding the water out of the garden hose, I coil it inside the little "house" I made to keep it from freezing. Also, since the cow's water tank was a 100-gallon tank, I half-filled it with sand because I didn't want to heat so much water. I insulated the sides of the tank and covered about half of the top with wood. Finally, I dropped a submersible tank heater into the water tank. These little heaters are thermostatically controlled and keep the water from freezing. Of course, they can use a lot of electricity, which is one reason I spent so much time trying to insulate the tank.

Several of the barn doors were also in need of repair. The back door kept coming off its track and was starting to fall apart. So I made a set of doors out of some scrap wood that a friend gave us. I have learned the importance of cross bracing barn doors or they will just warp on you. I also refurbished the beautiful front barn doors (with the characteristic cross pieces making an "X") by replacing the rotten wood and painting them.

The other barn work has involved making it safer for children. I repaired a ladder leading up to the hayloft. I also sealed off many of the "hay drops." These are square holes in the hay loft floor about 3 feet x 3 feet that let you throw hay down to the animals below. Since I didn't want any of my precious children to fall down these holes and land on the concrete below, I wrapped chicken wire around most of them. For the drops I actually use, I made a heavy wooden cover that can be lifted only by an adult.

The barn still isn't fixed up totally. It reminds me of something that one of my children said a few years back. On the back of a tube of Crest toothpaste it reads, "Squeeze tube from the bottom and flatten it as you go up." Jeannie, who was about seven at the time, misread it, and thought it said, "Squeeze tube from the bottom and flatten it as you *grow* up." I guess she expected that one tube of toothpaste to last all of her growing up years. Well, in the same way, I guess the barn fixing-up will last me a pretty long time, too.

Chapter 13
Stuff That Goes On Inside the House

Every time Susie visits a Living History museum (like Old World Wisconsin near Milwaukee) or attends any kind of old-fashioned gathering (like a Steam Tractor Show or a historical reenactment of some kind) she gets more "turned on" to the old ways of doing things. So it's not surprising that when we finally moved to our own farmstead that she wanted to try doing things the old-fashioned way. Let me share with you what we've learned so far in this part of our journey to self-sufficiency. (We tend to call it "self-sufficiency," although a more accurate phrase would probably be "self-sufficiency due to God's power and grace.")

Making Soap

Susie found a recipe for making soap in a magazine that she used to take called *Gentle Spirit*. Now, she had the motivation *and* the recipe! I knew she was serious when she asked me to separate and keep the clean fat when I butchered our chickens one year. "What you going to do with this junk?" I asked. "Make soap!" was her enthusiastic reply. You're kidding, I thought. But I kept the fat out for her anyway.

It wasn't long before the not-so-sweet smell of boiling chicken fat filled the house. "What in the world are you making?" I asked. "Soap," she said. Oh no, I thought. I could picture me going to school after using some of this smelly soap. I could just see students in my Marketing Research class lift their heads, sniff around and ask, "Is someone boiling chicken fat around here?" However, that scenario didn't pan out because the soap making was a complete failure. Susie's brew never did turn into soap, it just stayed a gooey mess and I ended up having to throw it into the woods. Even after a year it was still there. I guess not even animals want to mess with that stuff.

So what happened? Why didn't it turn into soap? Seems that the problem lay in the recipe. You see, Susie used just chicken fat (no beef fat, which is not what the recipe called for) in her first attempt to make soap. Adding chicken fat to a soap recipe makes the resulting soap really soft. With nothing but chicken fat I guess it was just too soft. Actually, Susie may have made the first batch of homemade liquid soap, I don't know.

Susie was disappointed, but persistent. She discovered a better recipe and learned more about making soap by talking to friends who had actually made (and used!) it. For anyone interested in making soap, we highly recommend the little book by Merilyn Mohr entitled *The Art of Soap Making* (see the Recommended Reading List for details).

First, we had to gather the ingredients. The most important one is beef fat. Beef fat makes the hardest soap (great for bar soap) which also lasts the longest. Chances are you don't have thirty pounds of beef fat lying around your house. But your butcher or grocery store meat department does. And they sell it, too. We bought ours right around July 4th, and got a real deal. Seems they have tons of extra fat at this time due to the holiday and can't get rid of it as easily--could be true around Memorial Day, and other holidays as well. (Don't just buy it off the meat display or you'll pay too much. The store will usually cut you a real good deal if you buy a lot. Make sure you get only beef fat, not mixed with pork.) I also bought cans of 100 % Lye Drain Cleaner. Don't be fooled; it has to be 100% lye, and not just say "lye" somewhere on the package. This is also found in most grocery stores near where they sell Liquid Plumber and other drain cleaners. It comes in a can, in dry crystals. We bought a few liters of olive oil too. Olive oil helps add some softening to the soap. The other things you need include some enamel or stainless steel pots, cheesecloth, a few old wooden spoons, shallow sturdy cardboard boxes (about 15" x 10"), a source of heat (got a stove?), and two candy thermometers (that you can buy at grocery or discount stores). Okay, ready to learn how to make soap?

First you have to "trim" all of that fat. Trimming just means to throw away all the meat and the really soft slimy fat. Only keep the hard dry fat. (It is okay though, if it has a few small bits of meat and stuff still on it. Just not much.) We did this on our front steps on a hot, sunny July morning. As the sun continued to climb into the sky, it got hotter, and the flies starting buzzing around all that fat. Not exactly the best situation! May I suggest that you trim your fat in the house?

After the clean fat is separated from the meat and trashy stuff, it is important to get rid of the waste. Since it was hot that day and I didn't feel like walking a long way, I made the mistake of just throwing this over in some weeds near the barn and house. You're probably thinking that I'm going to relate how it started to stink really badly. Not so. Instead, animals started coming in for the "goodies." I saw a fox slyly slinking around and chased it off. You don't want to do anything to attract foxes and coyotes near your barn, especially with chickens running around loose. Next time I'll make sure to throw it further away.

Now you need to render the trimmed fat. Rendering just means that you boil it down to get rid of any impurities left after you trimmed. To do this you fill a huge pot half full of fat, then add water to about three inches above the fat. Bring it to a boil and keep it boiling for about 5-6 hours. Warning: This will not smell good! Ever been to a greasy truck stop at rush-hour? If so, you've got a pretty good idea. While it is boiling, you need to keep it from scorching by stirring every 20 or 30 minutes. Make sure you keep adding plenty of water in the pot and keep it boiling well.

After it has boiled for 5-6 hours, you need to strain the liquid into another container covered with cheesecloth. We use a large strong rubber-band under the rim to hold the cheesecloth tight. Place a colander on top to catch all the unmelted hunks of fat and meat, or "hold back" the pieces of meat with the lid of the pot. You need to then let the fat cool overnight. In the morning the fat will be solid and sitting on top of the water. Take it off, scrape any impurities off the bottom, and freeze it if you don't intend to use it in the next day or so.

When you are ready to actually make soap, gather your ingredients together. The recipe is simple:

4 cups of melted beef fat
2 cups of olive oil
2 ¼ cups of cold water
¾ cup of lye.

But you have to add them in a very specific way! Let me tell you how.

While wearing rubber gloves, measure the lye and pour it into a glass, enamel, or stainless steel pot holding the cold water. Be very careful not to get lye on your skin, because it will cause a burn. (Keep vinegar handy to pour over your skin if you get splashed with lye.) This is going to set off a pretty strong chemical reaction and the mixture will get fairly hot (around 150-180 degrees F). Stir this mixture with a wooden spoon, making sure you are in a well-ventilated area. It is best to do this outside. Don't use your favorite wooden spoon, because the lye will damage the wood and you should not use it for cooking again. Keep all children and animals away from this mixture. Even though this mixture is very caustic, it will blend with the fat to make totally safe soap--trust me! **Use only an enamel, glass, or stainless steel pot, though**. The mixture will react with other metals. We look for these pots at yard sales. But be careful not to buy a pot if the enamel is chipped on the inside of the pot.

While the lye-water mixture is cooling, melt your fat back to a liquid state slowly. Don't scorch it. Use low or medium low heat--it will only take 5 or 10 minutes to melt. Add the olive oil, and cool to around 98 degrees F. You now have two pots, one with fat/olive oil and one with lye/water. When both pots are between 95-100 degrees F (use your candy thermometer to make sure!) you are ready to mix them. To do this, SLOWLY pour a small stream of lye/water into the fat/olive oil, stirring constantly, until all the lye/water has been added.

Continue to stir, nonstop, the combined mixture for ten

minutes. Then check to see if it's ready. You do this by "tracing" the liquid. How do you trace? Simple. Pick up your spoon and dribble a few drops of the mixture on top of the rest of the mixture (still in the pot). If it stays on top for a few seconds before disappearing into the liquid, then it's ready. If it doesn't stay on top, then keep stirring until it is ready. All of this stirring can take up to two hours, so don't quit in frustration. If the temperatures are right it usually only takes 15 or 20 minutes.

When the liquid is ready (using your "tracing" test) it is time to stir in any fragrance, if you want to. We have added musk, pine, rose, lemon, orange, and lavender essential oils. You don't have to add any fragrance, though. You are now ready to pour the liquid into your cardboard boxes (that are lined with plastic garbage bags). We grease the garbage bags with Vaseline® to keep the soap from sticking. Be careful, this stuff isn't soap yet, and can still burn you!

Take your filled boxes somewhere where they won't be disturbed and cover them with a stiff piece of cardboard, and some old towels or a blanket to keep the soap mixture from cooling too quickly. Don't mess with it for 24 hours. Don't even peek. After 24 hours cut the now-harder stuff into bars while wearing rubber gloves (it's still not soap!). Stack the bars on their sides in some way that air can circulate freely and let them age for a month.

At the end of the month your soap is ready. And you don't even have to wear rubber gloves while using it! You can also drop a couple of bars of soap into your washer, let it melt a bit as the washer fills, and use it for washing clothes. If you are just going to wash clothes with your soap, change the recipe to six cups of melted beef fat and leave out the olive oil. It'll save you a few bucks and your clothes won't care if the soap is soft or not! Or keep the olive oil in, and you'll be able to make more soap with less rendering. The clothes get really clean, and smell really clean. If you have hard water (we do), add 1/4 cup borax to each load, or you might have the soap sticking to your clothes. Just drop the soap into the water and let it agitate a minute, then remove the bars before you add the clothes.

It really works. You ought to try it, if nothing else, just so you can impress the clerks at your local grocery store. When we bought stuff to make soap, Susie or I would say, "Yeah, we're going to make our own soap." The clerks would stare at us in wide-eyed disbelief (as if we had just said we were going to build the U.S. space station out of milk cartons) and say, "You're kidding! How can you make your own soap?"

Our best advice is to get a good recipe and stick to it. This is no time for lots of creativity. Sure you can add any spices or fragrances you feel like, but don't mess around with the amounts of the basic ingredients. For example, don't say, "Gee, I'd like a really strong soap. Guess I'll add twice the lye Steve recommended!" Do that and you'll probably end up at your local hospital burn center.

Making Butter

Our first attempt at making butter was during those few weeks we had the first milk cow, A Moo Blossom Patience Bonnie (see Chapter 9 if you've forgotten our friend A Moo, etc.). We got all different kinds of advice about how to make butter and I think we must have tried them all, not with much success. Most people said the easiest thing to use was an electric mixer, but all we came up with was whipped cream. We never were successful making butter from A Moo's milk.

When we got Molly (remember our sweet, adorable, friendly Molly?) we tried our hand at making butter once again. But I was ready this time! For one of Susie's birthdays I surprised her with an antique crank-type butter churn that I found sitting on the shelf of a local antique shop. It only cost me $60, and it was a real antique. To try it out, we brought in some of Molly's milk, and let it sit in the refrigerator overnight. In the morning, we skimmed off the cream (using a bulb baster) and poured it into the churn. Susie and the children turned and turned that little crank trying to make butter. It never turned into butter. After talking to people, we discovered that our problem had probably been that we let the cream get too warm and that we didn't turn long enough.

The thing that has worked the best for us, is also very simple and unromantic (no need for antique appliances or anything!). We now keep the cream really cool in the refrigerator. We fill a half-gallon glass jar about 1/3 full of cream, put the top on and shake it. Correction: put the top on *really* tight and shake it. Children take turns walking around the house, shaking the jar. Our little children can't do it because they can't keep up a constant shake.

As this shaking is going on, the cream will get really foamy. Don't stop shaking. You'll know you are about there when you see little flecks of butter on the sides of the jar. But still don't stop shaking. In a couple of minutes (it usually takes us 20 minutes total of shaking) you open your jar and you'll see a big blob floating on top. That's butter!

Pour off the buttermilk and place the butter in a bowl, and pour a thin stream of ice cold water on it. You then start "working" the butter with a spoon or butter paddle. We bought a German butter paddle because we thought it would be necessary and save some time. A spoon works just as well. "Working" the butter just means you are sort of squishing or kneading the butter, while injecting a small stream of water every now and then onto it. You then pour that water out of the bowl. Repeat the process maybe ten times or so, until the water that you pour off looks clear. What you're trying to do with this "working" is to get the rest of the buttermilk out of the butter. If you don't do this, your butter will spoil faster.

After you have good clean butter, you just salt it and squish it around a bit more to work the salt throughout the butter. You're done! It tastes just like the butter in the store, assuming your milk was fresh. Basically, it will taste just as good (or just as bad) as your milk. If you milked your cow with a bunch of fly spray around, your milk and your butter will taste like fly spray. If you didn't bring in your milk right away from the barn, your milk and your butter will taste like the barn.

Just reading this account of making butter may make it sound hard and complicated. But in reality it is easy and fun and is one of the things that Susie and the children enjoy the most. If you don't want to keep a cow around but still want to make butter, don't give up. Just find a dairy farmer in your area. Chances are they will be willing to sell you some fresh, raw, non-homogenized, non-pasteurized milk right out of their milk bulk tank. Don't be paranoid about dying due to the milk being raw and unprocessed; people didn't die for thousands of years before pasteurization! Put the milk in jars, let it sit a day in the refrigerator until the cream rises, skim off the cream, and then follow the recipe I've provided.

I was a little squeamish to try our first butter. Could it really be as good as from the store? Didn't we need to add something else? Besides, I had seen the cow and knew she was just a smelly old cow. How could her butter possibly taste good? It did. I have come to realize that homemade stuff can taste just as good, and often better, than stuff you buy in the store. My reluctance to believe that simple truth is probably due to our culture's complete reliance on the wisdom of big business and experts. "Surely the big dairies know something about making butter that the average person couldn't ever learn." "Surely Proctor and Gamble know something about making soap that I could never hope to understand." We lean on experts even when it's not necessary! Like in doing things (e.g., making butter) that our grandparents and their parents did for thousands of years. Don't be intimidated to try "new" things. They aren't really new, they're just new to you.

Making Salves

Susie has manufactured lip balm and hand cream right at home. Our recipes call for the following:

Lip Balm

1 ½ tablespoons melted cocoa butter
½ cup olive oil
2 tablespoons melted beeswax

Hand Cream
   ¼ cup melted beeswax
   1 ½ cups olive oil

Beeswax can be found in lots of places. If you can't find a closer source try Lapp's Bee Supply Center, 500 South Main Street, Reeseville, WI 53579. A small amount is all you need, unless you also plan to make candles.

Making the lip balm and hand cream are really quite simple. You melt down beeswax in a double boiler (a coffee can with beeswax sitting inside a pot of boiling water). In a separate pan you heat olive oil and/or the cocoa butter on medium low heat (don't bring it anywhere near a boil!). You then pour the melted, measured beeswax into the other pan. This will cause the beeswax to harden again temporarily because the olive oil/cocoa butter is not as hot as the beeswax. Heat the mixture until it has re-melted. You keep stirring the combined mixture, with the pan on medium-low heat, until they are well-mixed. When they are mixed, your lip balm is ready. The recipe we found for hand cream recommended beating it with a spoon or whisk as it cooled to make it lighter and fluffy. If you do not beat the hand cream, it will have a consistency much like petroleum jelly, which is great as a baby cream/petroleum jelly-type product.

Now simply pour it into the containers you have ready. We just use empty little plastic containers that we have. If you use plastic, remember not to heat the mixture at a high temperature or it will melt your containers, a messy situation indeed!

Susie also makes a salve with healing properties for cuts, burns, rashes, etc. She starts with the same recipe as the hand cream (¼ cup melted beeswax with 1 ½ cups olive oil). Here's how she does it. She picks plantain, chickweed, and comfrey leaves. Comfrey is so easy to grow. In fact, it pretty much takes over wherever it is planted. Plantain is a common weed that is found in your yard, driveway, and just about everywhere. Chickweed is a common plant also, found in yards and fields. You just need someone to point them out to you or you can look them up in an herb book. Susie tears leaves from the plants into small pieces.

She then fills a quart jar with these broken leaves and pours olive oil to the very top of the jar. If you leave some air space in the top of the jar, the mixture can mold. And, if you pack the jar too tightly with leaves, the oil won't have much of a chance to penetrate into the leaves. Use a non-metal knife, or even just a stick, to move the leaves around a little and let the oil get to all the leaves. Now tighten the lids and let the jars sit at least six weeks, preferably in a dark, cool place. Put an old towel or rag under the jar, in case it leaks a bit. At the end of six weeks you pour off the "olive oil" to use, throwing away the leaves. It will smell bad, but don't worry! It hasn't gone bad. To make the salve Susie mixes the melted beeswax and this "olive oil," following the same directions for melting, combining, and reheating as for the lip balm and hand cream.

If this recipe doesn't seem soft enough for your family, use less beeswax or more olive oil (if too soft, add beeswax). It is very easy just to melt the mixture back down, add more oil or beeswax, and re-pour. You can do the same for the lip balm and hand cream. Experiment until you find the consistency you like best.

Putting Up Food for the Winter

We store a number of vegetables for the winter months. We generally wait until the first frost before we dig everything up, because our storage spot is too warm in August to do them much good. We dig the potatoes and gently brush the dirt off. A little dry dirt on the skins is good. If you're a perfectionist like me, you will want to wash them. Don't. We store the potatoes in little rigid mesh plastic crates (just like the little crates that hold four gallons of milk when it is delivered to grocery stores) so that air can circulate around them freely throughout the winter. It's important to place them into these crates gently. You don't want to bruise them or they won't last long.

Keeping carrots throughout the winter has not been totally

successful for us. We have tried burying them in a bucket of sand which we kept in a dark, cool place in the basement. The carrots started sprouting on us during the winter months. This year we are going to try another method. We will wash them, get them good and dry, and store them in plastic bags. We'll see if we have better success.

We pull our onions out of the ground when their tops are brown and falling over and put them on the basement floor for a couple of weeks to dry. We know they are ready to store when we see several layers of brown skin on them. Then we cut the tops off and store them in mesh bags or in a crate.

The potatoes, carrots and onions are stored in a root cellar that I made in one corner of the basement. I chose the further-most corner from the furnace. After enclosing the area with a wall, I insulated the walls and ceiling well. The room has a window in it which we open in the fall and winter as needed to keep the room around 36° F.

We also blanch (put in boiling water or over steam for a few minutes) and freeze peas, corn, carrots, celery, and broccoli. We have found that we can use the broccoli in casseroles, but not for much else; it gets too mushy for our tastes.

We can a number of fruits and vegetables each fall. I've always thought it should be called "glass jarring" instead of "canning"; don't see many tin cans around while we are doing this, just a bunch of mason jars. Anyway, we "can" mostly peaches, applesauce, jams, and tomatoes. I would fill you in on all the details of how we do this, but you would be better off talking to your local extension agent or reading about it in a book. Times and temperatures depend too much on altitude, varieties chosen, etc.

We also dry some fruits including apples, bananas, and peaches. Drying apples for us has been better than canning or freezing them. This is a super simple job, yet rewarding in terms of flavor and ease of use later. We slice the fruit, and without dipping them in anything or adding anything, place them on the shelves of our dehydrator. Actually, because of our family size, we own two dehydrators with twelve shelves in each. We turn the dehydrator on, and let it do all the work. At the end of the period (about six hours for apples, about 24 hours for bananas and peaches) we have wholesome, pure dried fruit that will last a long time. They're great as snacks and work wonderfully (meaning non-messy!) on trips. For our recipes that call for apples, Susie just rehydrates them by letting them soak in water for a while.

Making Candles

Susie makes our candles using pure beeswax. To do this, she buys big blocks of beeswax. Susie wanted to make elegant tapered candles, but had a lot of trouble finding a source of metal candle molds for this type. She finally found them in a catalog put out by Brushy Mountain Bee Farm (610 Bethany Church Road, Moravian Falls, NC 28654). These molds, which make eight candles at a time, work fine. We did drill the holes in the bottom of the mold, where the wick comes out, a little larger to make it easier to slide the wick into the hole. You may be able to pick up the wick material at a local craft store, but it will probably be cheaper if you buy spools of it from the same source as your beeswax or candle molds. Craft stores usually sell the wrong type of wick (it is made for paraffin candles instead of beeswax).   To make candles, Susie simply melts the beeswax, using a double boiler (a coffee can filled with beeswax, sitting in a pan of boiling water) because beeswax is flammable. Susie takes the wicks, waxes the end of them, and sticks them through the hole in the bottom of the candle mold. It is easiest if you put the waxed end into the hole from the bottom, not down from the top. Cut your wick long enough to have some to tie around a stick or pencil at the top, to keep the wick straight.

Making candles is not hard. Our failures have been relatively few. At first, we didn't keep the wick tight enough. As a result, instead of the wick staying in the exact center of the candle, it sort of wound its way down and around inside the candle anyway it wanted to. Some of the wick even lay on the outside of the candle, not a real professional looking job! Also, we had some candles break on us as we got them out of the mold. Why? Our problem was that we were, in error, filling the molds in two steps. In the first step, we would pour just a little wax in the bottom of the mold and let it harden. We hoped this would prevent the rest of the wax from running out the wick hole (which is at the bottom of the mold). In the second step, we would add the rest of the wax to the mold. Apparently, the two sets of wax weren't uniting well where they met. We have solved that problem now in the following way. We put a large knot in the end of the wick string (right outside the end of the mold) and that keeps the wax from running out the wick hole. To remove candles from the mold, dip the mold in a large pot of very hot water for 30 seconds or so. Cut the knot off the bottom, then gently pull out the candles. It helps greatly if you spray a vegetable oil spray into the mold before pouring the wax.

Herbs

In attempting to live a more natural, organic, simple life, we have found herbs serve our needs well. We grow echinacea, catnip, chamomile, horehound, lemon balm, comfrey, peppermint, raspberry (for raspberry leaves as well as raspberries), sage, and fennel. Most herbs are supposed to be perennials (meaning they come back every year) but it doesn't work out that way for us way up here. We always have to replant horehound, peppermint, and fennel, and sometimes have to replant chamomile.

Some herbs require drying, and some are used fresh to make tinctures. Tinctures are concentrated medicines in liquid form. For teas, you dry the leaves of most herbs, although some herbs require you to dry things other than leaves: for echinacea you dry the roots, for fennel you dry the seeds, and for chamomile you dry the flower tops. For catnip, horehound, lemon balm, peppermint, sage, and raspberry leaves, Susie goes out on a dry, warm morning after the dew dries off the leaves and picks off the leaves and/or stems. She ties a string around each bunch, using a rubber band to keep them together, and sticks them in a paper bag so that the stems are sticking out of a hole in the bottom of the bag. She then hangs them upside down in a dry, warm place. It usually takes anywhere from one week to a month for them to dry throughly, depending on the dryness of the leaves and the room. After totally dry, she places them in clean dry jars. These will keep indefinitely, but she likes to replace them with new batches each year.

So, as you can see, things are kept hopping inside the house. We enjoy doing things the old-fashioned way and find the experience to be quite rewarding. Try it, you may like it too!

Chapter 14
Just Living Here

I'm happy to report that we don't just work on this farm. It's a beautiful place set in a beautiful part of the country and we find time to play and enjoy ourselves in it. In this chapter I'll share with you some of the things we do. Since we don't own a TV (by choice), we get some interesting questions about how we spend our time. One girl, after asking three times, "You mean you really don't have any TV?" commented a few minutes after we walked away, "What do they do? Just sit around and look at each other?" Well, yes we do look at each other. Is there anything more fun than watching an eighteen month-old toddle around jabbering as he plays with kitchen utensils? But we do other things as well.

Before I tell you what we do, let me tell you what we don't do. We aren't "into" what most people seem to be "into" today: running their children to get lessons and/or play T-ball, dance, soccer, tap, ballet, cheerleading, football, hockey, scouts, 4-H, wrestling, gymnastics, twirling or the 1001 clubs and organizations that are vying for kid's attention (and your money!). You may do those things and that's probably okay for you as long as all of that running doesn't start to rule or control your family. If it does, you've lost in my opinion. We like to do things together as a family. Our children like it best that way and so do their parents!

We are blessed to be in an area of unusual beauty. With many lakes and rivers in the area, we've taken up canoeing. We realized the potential after taking a memorable canoe ride with the Berglund family one evening a few summers ago. On that trip we lazily floated down the scenic Brule River, entranced with the beauty of the river and the gracefulness of an eagle flying overhead. After that, we just had to buy a canoe! So we did. We bought Robin's old canoe. He even delivered it to our house for us. When he unloaded it, he noted that it had been stored for the last few weeks upside down, and he hadn't realized that it was lying on an ants' nest. "No problem," I said. "I'll just hose them right out."

The children and I hosed down and hosed down those little enclosed parts of the canoe in the front and back. Ants just kept coming out. To insure that we got all those little creatures, I grabbed an old can of ant spray and sprayed the rest of it into the cracks where the ants had been. After a while we didn't see any more ants emerging (either alive or dead) and we assumed that we had gotten the last of them. It pays to be thorough!

Before we could try the canoe out, we had a few things to buy. Like life jackets for all seven of us. I didn't want to buy those little cheap orange puffy vests because I've found them to be very uncomfortable - I always feel like I am wearing a weather balloon around my neck when I have to put one on. When I was growing up, I wore water ski jackets (not to school, but when I went water skiing with George Aslinger), which I found to be much more comfortable. So we bought those special thin water ski jackets for everyone. Cost me a fortune, too! But if we weren't going to be comfortable, there was no reason to do it in the first place.

Along with the life jackets, we also had to buy paddles. Usually, it only takes two paddles to propel a canoe. We bought four. Then we bought four child-sized ones. Now more people can enjoy the fun of paddling. You should see us heading down the river, with paddles sticking out all over the place. Looks sort of like an old-fashioned galley; you know, those ships that are propelled by long rows of oars pulled by slaves or convicts.

With a canoe, life jackets, and paddles, we were ready! We decided to take our very first family canoe ride. First, I had to load the canoe onto the top of my car. Now that doesn't sound all that hard. But remember that I own a full-size van, and it's a long way to the top of the car! It took a lot of grunting and shoving to get the canoe in position up there. Even though I had placed several pieces of cardboard under the canoe, I still heard the distinctive sound of paint being scraped off as the canoe settled on top. "Great. A place for rust to start forming this winter," I mumbled to myself.

I didn't own any of those nifty tie-downs yet. So I used baling twine to tie the canoe to the car. In fact, I used tons of baling twine. It probably looked like a hay baler came upon my car in the middle of a field, baled it, and ejected it out the back. In my defense, I didn't want that canoe to slide off as we were driving down the highway. Even with all that twine, it still moved a little bit when I pushed it. Oh well, that's the best I could do.

After everyone went to the bathroom (or *claimed* to have gone to the bathroom) we loaded up the life jackets, oars, children, bug spray, jackets, towels, a few gallons of water, and drove out of the driveway. All the children were bouncy! So was the canoe on the top of the car. Since it was such a long canoe, a good bit of it hung down in front of the windshield for me to watch. I watched it bounce around as we drove the back roads. When we hit the main highway, I watched the front of the canoe slowly start to lift, just like I have watched the front of jet airplanes slowly start to lift during take off. I'm always relieved when planes start to lift. I wasn't equally enthused about my canoe taking off! So I did what every man in America would do in those circumstances: "Quick Susie, stick your hand out of the window and help me hold on to the canoe!" This maneuver prevented "take off" but caused all the blood to drain, it seemed permanently, from our arms.

"How much further?" Susie asked. "About 35 minutes," I replied. But after a while I got out and tightened up the baling twine some more. That seemed to help the "take off" problem. Nothing much helped the side-to-side movement (caused by the silly thing resting on cardboard; whose idea was that?!).

We reached the landing, the place to put the canoe into the water. It wasn't the same place we had gone with the Berglunds, though. With only one car, we didn't have the luxury of leaving one car downstream and one upstream (like we had done with the Berglunds). Thus, we were planning on "putting in" and paddling

weren't moving. The current was just too hard. Susie started laughing. So did I. In fact, we almost got hysterical. That didn't calm the children's fears, however. Also, I learned that when you laugh you can't paddle as fast, which resulted in us "losing ground."

Finally, in desperation, I jumped out of the canoe a second time, and grabbed the front of the canoe. The people on the bank watched. Using about all my strength, I became a tug (like Bogart, again) and pulled the canoe back to the landing we had left only a few minutes earlier. Everyone got out of the canoe and I dragged it back to the car. After the hard chore of loading the canoe back on top (with the usual scraping noises) I tied it down securely. The younger children had stopped crying and were happy to be on dry land again. Of course, the older two were disappointed and asked very irrelevant questions like "Daddy, we didn't get to go for a very long ride! Why not?" and "When can we go again?" Like I said, very irrelevant.

We did get home again, though. And we did get over that canoe trip. I learned that the stretch of the Brule we were trying to canoe that day was one of its roughest stretches! In fact, a brochure put out by the Wisconsin Department of Natural Resources sums it up this way:

> The river itself has two distinct personalities. The upper river (the southern portion) flows through miles of coniferous bog and is fed by numerous springs. These springs are the source of the clear water of the Brule. This part of the river falls gently at the rate of three feet per mile for thirty miles. Between U.S. Highway "2" and County Road "FF", there is a dramatic change. When the river crosses the Copper Range, it begins a fall of 328 feet in the nineteen miles to Lake Superior. Here, flashing cascades tumble over rocks and ledges between steep river bluffs forested with aspen and balsam fir.

Our first canoe ride with the Berglunds was on the upper river. Our "disastrous" trip was on the lower portion. No wonder we had such a different experience!

We got smart and scouted out some much more placid rivers.

Since then we have made a few changes. We strap the canoe to the little trailer, using those wonderful tie-down straps you can buy (no more baling twine or tying on top of the van for me!). And we only canoe in stretches that we have carefully checked out beforehand. If it's questionable, then the older children and I canoe it first. We have had many wonderful canoe rides that everyone enjoyed. Our problem now is that we have outgrown our canoe. With eight people in it, it became too crowded and tipsy, and God blessed us with another baby recently. Nine just won't fit! So we are trying to find a second canoe.

Another thing we enjoy doing is going for bike rides. Everyone over the age of five has their own bike. The baby generally rides on the back of Susie's bike and the other small children (usually two) ride in a little Burly® trailer behind my bike. So far, when it is time for a new baby to "take over" in Susie's carrier, one of my passengers is ready to ride his/her own bicycle. We usually ride on back country roads. To get all those bikes and the child trailer to our destination, I use the little trailer that I pull behind my van. That little trailer has come in handy for so many things.

Here in northern Wisconsin, we have a lot of snowmobile/ATV trails, but the ones we have tried are too rough to ride bikes on. These trails have something like cinders as a roadbed, and it's easy for the little ones to get bogged down in them.

We really enjoy bicycling because the world moves by at such a slow pace. You get a chance to really see things that you miss as you drive by in a car. It's also nice and quiet. We always take water along and stop for little breaks and listen to the birds sing. Of course it's not always idyllic. There are mosquitoes, flies, hot sunshine, and speeding cars at times. Also, the legs can get pretty tired, especially if you are trailering a few children in a trailer. But overall it's a lot of fun.

We also enjoy walking. We have cleared seven walking paths through our woods and fields. Hardly a day goes by that Susie and I don't go for a walk. We have several nice trails down to the river on our property. We are in the process of naming the trails (like Elijah's Circle) and putting up little markers just for fun. Again, there are mosquitoes and flies to contend with. But we've also seen bears, foxes, coyotes, minks, eagles, ducks, Canadian geese, hawks, and many other forms of wildlife on our walks. The wildflowers are also a joy to walk among. We are blessed with the usual buttercups, violets, goldenrod (although with sinus problems we aren't sure how much of a blessing they are at times!) and daisies, in addition to hundreds of "unique" wildflowers like wild roses, bluets, columbine, orange hawkweed, least hop clover, Canada anemone, blue-eyed grass, and forget-me-nots. Then you have the sky, sunsets, clouds, stars, and moon to enjoy as well. Who needs TV, anyway?

Right around the house there are plenty of things for us to do. We built a small campfire area, using some of the rocks we picked up from the shores of Lake Superior. On cool fall nights we sit around the fire, singing songs and looking at the stars. On cold winter days, a fire is built to help warm up little hands that are cold from playing in the snow. I made the campfire area real close to the house so we would tend to use it more (and so I could look out during the night to make sure the fire was really put out--I'm a worrier that way). I built some benches that surround the campfire out of scrap wood we had in the barn. Nothing real fancy. It only took me a few hours to build five of them. I placed several along the walking paths and down by the river, too.

We also have a sandbox. It's pretty big, about 10 feet by 10 feet. I figured why not let everyone have plenty of room to play? I built it, like I have so many other things, out of scrap lumber I found in the barn--it took me about 30 minutes to build. The children really enjoy it. Sad to say, so do the cats. They think it's a bathroom. We've tried several methods to stop the cats from using our sandbox as a litter box. First we covered it with a tarp. A nice plan, except children kept forgetting to pull it back over the sandbox when they were through playing. Also, the cats could crawl in there if we didn't seal it up really carefully, something little children can't do well. Our second attempt at stopping the cats was to erect a screen tent over the whole sandbox. We shoveled sand around its base, making it virtually cat-proof. I thought we really had the answer with that. It not only was going to keep the cats out, it also should cut down on mosquito and fly bites on the children. With the top of the tent solid, it made a snug place to play when it was softly raining outside. Problem? The cats really didn't like me covering up their bathroom. How would you like it if someone waltzed into your house and nailed your bathroom door shut? What would you do? Probably just knock the door down. Well, the cats did about the same thing, only they used their claws. With a big jagged rip in one side, the cats were able to continue using it for their bathroom. Finally, I broke down and made a cover for the sandbox by building a frame and stretching a tarp over it. After the children are finished playing they just move the cover over the sandbox. No more problems with the cats (except when the children forget to cover it!).

Next to the sandbox is a swing set that gets a lot of use. Also there are several very large willow trees right there, with long branches that are perfect for climbing on and jumping off. A mature apple tree is also situated close by, which is just the thing for "little" climbers.

What was missing? The children were always asking me to help them make a seesaw. They would even get pieces of wood and try to fashion one themselves, often resulting in a pretty unsafe toy. So, I built them a seesaw. I dug a hole 3 ½ feet in the ground and secured the two poles of the seesaw in 80 pounds of concrete. What I'm trying to say is that the seesaw is there to stay. It'll probably outlast the house. Now that would be good news except for the fact that playing on the seesaw hasn't worked out well. It still seems that children are always getting hurt on it or just don't play well with it. I don't know what the future holds for the seesaw.

The children also play in the barn. I installed a tire swing up in the hayloft that they really enjoy. They also like to ride bikes up there in the winter. Imagine, it's cold outside with three feet of snow on the ground, yet the children are riding in what amounts to an indoor riding arena. It's great.

We spend a good bit of time watching and trying to identify birds. To make that more enjoyable (and to get more birds to look at) I've installed a few hummingbird feeders near the kitchen and a large bird feeder in the front yard. We see many kinds of birds in the front feeder, including Evening Grosbeak, American Goldfinch, Eastern Meadowlark, Baltimore Oriole, Robin, Cardinal, Rose-breasted Grosbeak, Purple Finch, Black-capped Chickadee, Dark-eyed Junco, Bluejay, Vireo, Brown Thrasher, Cedar Waxwing, Brown-headed Cowbird, Hermit Thrush, Sparrow (House, Chipping, Tree, White-throated, Song, Fox), Red-winged Blackbird, and Red-breasted Nuthatch. Of course, the cats kill some of the birds. Recently we noticed a rat near the back of the house, which was probably hanging around to eat the bird feed. That has caused me to slow down on feeding the birds. I love birds, but don't want to attract rats that will probably find their way into the house. That wouldn't be fun!

Part of the joy of living on a farm is a sense of seclusion and protection for the children. We have lots of trees around the house, but still feel the need for more (to block the views to the highway, to offer a bit more protection from the winter storms, etc.). Along the road side of our house we decided to plant some hybrid willow trees. It was claimed that they would grow very rapidly, even 5-8 feet a year. We had visions of big beautiful trees in only three or four years. I dug big holes, backfilled with a mixture of manure and the soil that was already there, and staked the trees out. I faithfully watered them, and caged them to keep animals from eating them. They died. The next year, we decided to go with Caragana bushes. These were supposed to grow 15-20 feet tall and form a thick screen. I planted, watered, and basically gave them tender-loving care for weeks. They died. What was causing all this death? I was pretty much in the dark, until one day when we had August Ahola, the man who had owned our farm for years and years, over for dinner. I told him of our troubles and he said, "Yeah, that is where the highway used to run. Right out there (pointing to where I had unsuccessfully planted trees and shrubs)." At last I had my answer. Those trees and shrubs probably grew down just to where the old highway is buried and then couldn't grow through the rock and asphalt.

I still wanted to plant some trees and talked to Jeff Berthiaume. He said he just went out into his woods, dug up some balsam trees, and transplanted them. Makes sense. You are transplanting trees that grow in this area and which have already survived several of our tough winters. So I tried it. I transplanted about a dozen of these trees and guess what? They are all still living. I don't expect fast growth, but at least they will grow. And they will provide good screen too.

We planted two crabapple trees right in front of the house to provide beauty and cut down a little on the sun's rays in the morning. After all, shady places are nice places to play. One is an Almey Flowering Crabapple, while the other is a Bechtel Flowering Crabapple. As with the other trees, I have given them tender loving care. One day I removed their wire cages to mow closer around them and must have forgotten to put the cages back where they belonged. Anyway, in a few days, Betsy was running in the yard, not watching where she was going, and ran right over the Almey. One of the other children ran into the house and said, "Daddy, Betsy just broke one of your trees." I ran outside and saw that the tallest and strongest branch of the tree was broken in two. Probably took two years off its growth. I was sad, but happy that Betsy wasn't hurt herself. Trees can't be more important than children. I did put the cages back on, however.

Our yard is a rather large one. We must have over three acres of grass to cut in addition to all the walking paths I've developed. I needed some way to cut that grass. When we first moved into the house, we considered our options. Basically, we could buy a push or riding lawn mower. We were all in favor of protecting the environment and getting more accustomed to working hard. As a result we decided to buy a nonpowered (except for "Steve" power) 18" reel-type mower. It only cost $40 at the local Target Store and was going to be the answer! We could cut all of our grass, use no electricity or gasoline, make no noise, and get a lot of good clean exercise in the process. I must say that Susie was much more enthusiastic about this project than I was. As a young boy, I had tried out a hand powered reel type mower, and found it to be hard to push but easy to get clogged with sticks or rocks. In fact, I found it quite frustrating!

But not to worry, said Susie, no doubt they have made all kinds of technological improvements in reel-type mowers in all those years. Looking back, I must say that I don't think that the net result of our sending men to the moon and all of our technical leaps in manufacturing and engineering has made the least little bit of difference to the design and manufacture of these little hand powered mowers.

I brought the thing home, put it together, and headed to the front yard. To be fair, it should be noted that the grass had grown up considerably by the time we finally decided on the mower, and it was no easy task to cut. In fact, all the grass had to be cut two times, or three times, or even four times, to get it all cut down nice and level. And it didn't help that it was hot that day. Susie was in the house, watching me from the front window. After a while, she came out and said, "I can see it's just not going to work. I'm sorry. Don't feel like you have to finish cutting it with that mower."

But I wanted to give it a chance and see exactly how much time and energy it would consume. It took me *tons* of time and energy just to cut a small section in the front yard. And the children, who were very enthusiastic about the whole idea just like their mom, could hardly even make the mower move. It's just a guess, but I figure it would take me about 20-25 hours to cut our grass each week with that mower. That wouldn't leave a whole lot of time for doing much else that needed to be done. In the end, we decided to get rid of that little mower and get a REAL mower.

The experience with the hand powered mower had taught me the importance of getting something with lots of power. So I started watching ads for a riding lawn mower. John Deere had its STX38 on sale for $1995 (that's a little more expensive than $40, I admit) and I bought one. The 38 means that it cuts a 38" swath at one pass (that's a little more than the 18" swath of the hand powered one, I admit!). Robin drove me in his pickup truck to bring the new mower home. I was ecstatic. I had something that would cut the grass, cut it evenly, and cut it quickly.

I was so excited that evening about my new mower that I cut every blade of grass I could find. I even started cutting grass where the previous owners hadn't cut. I started down the outside of my main fence (by the road) cutting and singing to myself. Until I hit a half-buried piece of pipe sticking out of the ground next to the fence, that is. It was such a jolt that it killed the mower. Upon inspection, I learned that I had slightly bent one of the mower deck shafts. The first night of use and I had bent one of the shafts! The lesson I learned is not to hold any of your possessions too closely or dearly. That's a lesson I'm afraid I need to learn and relearn. I tend to take good care of my possessions and want them to look nice and work great. They are just possessions, however, and they should never possess you! If they tear up, it's not the end of the world.

As it turns out that was a timely lesson for me. The very next day I walked into my garage and found four-year-old Betsy busily sanding my John Deere garden tractor with a piece of rough sandpaper. There were scratches all over the plastic hood. "See Daddy, I'm helping you!" she said. She sure was. She was making sure I learned my lesson about not getting too attached to this perfect-looking tractor. She didn't know any better. She was just sanding it because she had seen me scrape peeling paint off the house and garage in preparation for painting them. My response was, "Betsy, please don't sand my tractor anymore." That isn't the only response I wanted to give her. But it was the right one. My prayer is that God would help me respond as He would have me to, not the way I want to.

Parting Thoughts

We do have lots of fun on this farm. We are thankful that we have such a neat place to raise our children. The last few years have been growing ones for us and we look forward to the next few as well. I wonder what kinds of things we will get involved with next? What buildings will we build or tear down? What kinds of animals will we get or get rid of? What will we do differently in terms of crops and gardens?

What home businesses will we start? We've developed some criteria for any home businesses that we start:

① The business must meet a real need (for example, we're not going to be making and selling plastic Easter eggs).
② The business shouldn't require me to fly all over the country.
③ The business should be such that our children can go into the business with us or branch off it in some way as they get older.
④ The business should result in self-employment, not working for someone else.

What renovations or changes will we make in our farm house? What does the future hold in terms of climate? How will our community change? What new friends will we meet? Will we move to a new farm? It's exciting to think about. We don't know the answers to these questions, but God does. The answers are in His Hands. May we trust Him for the future.

We'll keep you posted.

Recommended Reading List

Back to Basics (1981), Reader's Digest. A good book which gives you the principles for doing just about everything on a small farm or homestead. Lots of good illustrations.

Build It Better Yourself (1977), by the editors of Organic Gardening and Farming®, Rodale Press, Inc. Need to build something? This book probably will tell you how. It includes information on building walks, walls, fences, gates, sheds, barns, greenhouses, cold frames, and many other items.

Cox, Jeff (1988), *How to Grow Vegetables Organically*, Rodale Press. An excellent book that will help you save your garden from insects, and do it safely!

DeBairacli Levy, Juliette (1991), *The Complete Herbal Handbook for Farm and Stable*, London: Faber & Faber. This book is like a veterinarian handbook, but with a herbal focus for remedies.

Emery, Carla, *The Encyclopedia of Country Living, ninth edition*, Sasquatch Books. I recommend that you write Carla directly to get a copy of this excellent book. In fact, if you are just going to buy one book to help you learn how to do things, this is it! She'll tell you how to butcher, raise just about every type of farm animal you can think of, grow and process fruits and vegetables, make soap, tan leather, and a million other things. She even has a list of hundreds of books, magazines, and newsletters that you may want to check out. It's the first source we check for most things. To order a copy write directly to: Carla Emery, Box 209, Kendrick, ID 83537.

Langer, Richard W. (1972), *Grow It!* New York: Saturday Review Press. The statement in the front of the book sums it up pretty well: "The beginner's complete in-harmony-with-nature small farm guide - from vegetable and grain growing to livestock care."

Mohr, Merilyn (1979), *The Art of Soap Making*, Buffalo, New York: Camden House Publishing. A great little book on how to make soap. Included are recipes for just about every type of soap you can imagine.

Ortho's Home Improvement Encyclopedia (1985), Karin Shakery, Editor, San Francisco: Ortho Books. This book will give you the confidence you need to do all sorts of home improvement projects including plumbing, electrical, carpentry, painting, general repair and maintenance, and designing.

Organic Plant Protection (1976), Roger B. Yepsen, Jr., Editor, Rodale Press. The title is self-explanatory.

Rodale's Illustrated Encyclopedia of Herbs (1987),Claire Kowalchik and William H. Hylton, Editors, Emmaus, Pennsylvania: Rodale Press. An excellent book on identifying, growing, harvesting and using herbs.

Rogers, Marc (1990), *Saving Seeds: The Gardener's Guide to Growing and Storing Vegetable and Flower Seeds*, Pownal, Vermont: Storey Communications, Inc. The book title says it all. If you want to save your own seeds, this is a good book for you.

Small Farmer's Journal, P.O. Box 1627, Sisters, Oregon 97759. An excellent journal (magazine) that comes out four times a year. I recommend subscribing and also buying all the back issues you can get your hands on. It's that good!

Castleberry Farms Press

Our primary goal in publishing is to provide wholesome books in a manner that brings honor to our Lord. We believe in setting no evil thing before our eyes (Psalm 101:3) and although there are many outstanding books, we have had trouble finding enough good reading material for our children. Therefore, we feel the Lord has led us to start this family business.

We believe the following: The Bible is the infallible true Word of God. That God is the Creator and Controller of the universe. That Jesus Christ is the only begotten Son of God, was born of the virgin Mary, lived a perfect life, was crucified, buried, rose again, sits at the right hand of God, and makes intercession for the saints. That Jesus Christ is the only Savior and way to the Father. That salvation is based on faith alone, but true faith will produce good works. That the Holy Spirit is given to believers as Guide and Comforter. That the Lord Jesus will return. That man was created to glorify God and enjoy Him forever.

We began writing and publishing in mid-1996 and hope to add more books in the future if the Lord is willing. All books are written by Mr. and Mrs. Castleberry.

We would love to hear from you if you have any comments or suggestions. Our address is at the end of this section. Now, we'll tell you a little about our books.

The Courtship Series

These books are written to encourage the active involvement of their parents as young adults seek a mate. The main characters are committed followers of Jesus Christ, and Christian family values are emphasized throughout. The reader will be encouraged to heed parental advice and to live in obedience to the Lord.

Jeff McLean: His Courtship

Follow the story of Jeff McLean as he seeks God's direction for his life. This book is written from a young man's perspective. A discussion of godly traits to seek in young men and women is included as part of the story. Paperback, 1998. ISBN 1-891907-05-0.

The Courtship of Sarah McLean

Sarah McLean is a nineteen-year-old girl who longs to become a wife and mother. The book chronicles a period of two years, in which she has to learn to trust her parents and God fully in their decisions for her future. Paperback, 2nd edition, 1997. ISBN 1-891907-00-X.

Waiting for Her Isaac

Sixteen-year-old Beth Grant is quite happy with her life and has no desire for any changes. But God has many lessons in store before she is ready for courtship. The story of Beth's spiritual journey toward godly womanhood is told along with the story of her courtship. Paperback, 1997. ISBN 1-891907-03-4.

New Books in this Series?

See our web site or write to us for our latest titles.

The Farm Mystery Series

Join Jason and Andy as they try to solve the mysterious happenings on the Nelson family's farm. These are books that the whole family will enjoy. In fact, many have used them as read-aloud-to-the-family books. Parents can be assured that there are no murders or other objectionable elements in these books. The boys learn lessons in obedience and responsibility while having lots of fun. There are no worldly situations or language, and no boy-girl relationships. Just happy and wholesome Christian family life, with lots of everyday adventure woven in.

Footprints in the Barn

Who is the man in the green car? What is going on in the hayloft? Is there something wrong with the mailbox? And what's for lunch? The answers to these and many other interesting questions are found in the book <u>Footprints in the Barn</u>. Paperback, 2001. ISBN 1-891907-01-8.

The Mysterious Message

The Great Detective Agency is at it once again, solving mysteries on the Nelson farmstead. Why is there a pile of rocks in the woods? Is someone stealing gas from the mill? How could a railroad disappear? And will Jason and Andy have to eat biscuits without honey? You will have to read this second book in the Farm Mystery Series to find out. Paperback, 1997. ISBN 1-891907-04-2.

Midnight Sky

What is that sound in the woods? Has someone been stealing Dad's tools? Why is a strange dog barking at midnight? And will the Nelsons be able to adopt Russian children? <u>Midnight Sky</u> provides the answers. Paperback, 1998. ISBN 1-891907-06-9.

Who, Me?

Who (or what) has taken Dad's watch and all the other things missing on the Nelson family farm? Should Dad invest in that fantastic money-making opportunity? And who are those new neighbors through the woods? Are they somehow responsible for the Nelsons' troubles? Read <u>Who, Me?</u> for answers to these and other tough questions. Paperback, 2001. ISBN 1-891907-10-7.

Weighty Matters
A thousand nails in a barn? Why is there a mess in the kitchen at midnight? Who is Molly Buford, anyway? Will the boys figure out why there are leeches in a firetruck? And does Dad have to give up blueberry cream pie forever? Weighty matters, to be sure, but not too hard for the Great Detective Agency! Paperback, 2003. ISBN 1-891907-13-1.

Other Books

Call Her Blessed
This book is designed to encourage mothers to consistently, day by day, follow God's will in their role as mothers. Examples are provided of mothers who know how to nurture and strengthen their children's faith in God. Paperback,. 1998. ISBN 1-891907-08-5.

The Delivery
Joe Reynolds is a husband and father striving to live a life pleasing to the Lord Jesus Christ. Having been a Christian only seven years, he has many questions and challenges in his life. How does a man working in the world face temptation? How does he raise his family in a Christ-honoring way? This book attempts to Biblically address many of the issues that

men face daily, in a manner that will not cause the reader to stumble in his walk with the Lord. The book is written for men (and young men) by a man – we ask men to read it first, before reading it aloud to their families. Paperback, 1999. ISBN 1-891907-09-3.

Our Homestead Story
The humorous account of one family's journey toward a more self-sufficient life-style with the help of God. Read about their experiences with cows, chickens, horses, sheep, gardening and more. Paperback, 2003. ISBN 1-891907-12-3.

For a catalog, order form, information on new titles, prices and shipping charges please contact us:

1) web:
   www.castleberryfarmspress.com

2) email:
   info@castleberryfarmspress.com

3) mail: Castleberry Farms Press,
   P.O. Box 337, Poplar, WI 54864